INVISIBLE
CONVERSATIONS

INVISIBLE CONVERSATIONS

HOW TO USE COMMUNICATION TO SUPPORT THOSE WITH INVISIBLE DISABILITIES

ALEXANDRA GUILLOT

NEW DEGREE PRESS

INVISIBLE CONVERSATIONS

How to Use Communication to Support Those with Invisible Disabilities

ISBN   978-1-63676-704-8   *Paperback*

            978-1-63730-063-3   *Kindle Ebook*

            978-1-63730-165-4   *Ebook*

To my best friend—I also call her Ma.

CONTENTS

———

INTRODUCTION

———

When I stepped foot onto my college campus, I felt invigorated by the unfamiliar surroundings. For the first time, I was hundreds of miles away from my home, away from anyone who knew me and my past. I was ready to leave my pain behind as I began to envision the future ahead of me. By coming to this new place, each conversation and interaction was like an opportunity to reinvent myself. No one knew who I was, only who I was going to be. I could pick and choose what parts of my identity to display for others and build a new version of myself for everyone but me. No one could see my disabilities by simply looking at me. I had invisible disabilities I could choose to reveal to others. Behind this self-assured façade, I would continue to carry the weight of my conditions and attempt to drown them out with the new opportunities ahead.

This charade began to falter as the pressures from campus life began to mount. As coursework and extracurricular responsibilities piled on, I felt myself starting to crack from the stress, and my pain came rushing back. The line I drew between myself and my disabilities was broken as I sustained my fourth concussion halfway through my first semester of freshman year.

As I sat in class, reeling from my latest concussion, I felt as though the future I had hoped for and had willed to happen was ripped away. I was thrown back into my past in the blink of an eye and was brought back to the start of a long, dark tunnel with the tiniest light of hope at the end of it. I could no longer avoid sharing my disabilities, as I was forced to disclose my conditions to receive accommodations for my classes.

The first emails, letters, and conversations were the hardest. I felt like an impostor, writing to my professors and faculty about my disabilities and how they could impact the semester ahead. When I came to school, I told stories of accomplishments and high hopes for my future during and after college. Now I wrote the reasons as to why I may not be able to live up to the expectations I had for myself, and others had for me. I grew fearful of the stigmatization and discrimination that could follow once I disclosed my conditions, as most people assume since I am young, I must be healthy.

Despite my young age, I have struggled with my health and wellbeing for most of my life. My largest hurdle has been my chronic pain condition called Amplified Musculoskeletal Pain Syndrome, or AMPS. Sometimes referred to as juvenile fibromyalgia or chronic widespread pain, the condition is characterized as localized or full-body pain, resulting from an abnormal and overactive pain reflex in children and adolescents.[1] [2] This abnormality can be caused by injuries, illnesses, and psychological stress.[3]

Having heard from dozens of young people and their parents who have grappled with AMPS, it is clear every case is unique. In my own situation, I believe I've developed AMPS as a result of psychological stress, as I struggled with general anxiety disorder from a very young age. My anxiety and chronic pain spurred each other on for over a decade of my life.

Looking beyond AMPS, I've also suffered from four concussions between high school and college, resulting in a diagnosis of post-traumatic stress disorder from so many injuries. Between all of these conditions and injuries, I've been a patient for a vast majority of my life.

For many years, I have avoided sharing my health history. I often feel lonely when sharing my invisible disabilities with others. Most times, this is a one-way dialogue as I trade the story of my past, present, and future of my conditions with the other person in exchange for their sympathies or understanding. While doing this, I feel as though I am the only one who must go through this process. On very rare occasions, someone has disclosed their own condition or disability to me, but only after I've shared my own disabilities first.

---

1   "Amplified Musculoskeletal Pain Syndrome (AMPS)," American College of Rheumatology, accessed January 14, 2021.

2   "AMPS Program Offered at PMC," Providence Medical Center, accessed January 14, 2021.

3   "Amplified Musculoskeletal Pain Syndrome (AMPS)," Children's Hospital of Philadelphia, accessed January 14, 2021.

While it can feel isolating to share my experiences, I now fear the outcomes of not opening up at all. Since coming to college, I've learned the only way I will be able to get support from others is if I disclose at least some information about my conditions. By silencing myself and my experiences, I would further play into the inconspicuousness of invisible disabilities. The stigmas surrounding young people with invisible illnesses would progress further as no one would be raising their voices to share their stories. In turn, acts of discrimination would grow as people with disabilities would go unnoticed and unsupported throughout every stage of their lives.

One in ten people are estimated to have a condition that can be considered an invisible disability. Looking closer, invisible disabilities are the most common types of disabilities amongst students and young people, as learning disabilities and mental disorders top the list of these conditions.[4] Without a visual clue, it is nearly impossible to understand how many people around us have invisible disabilities. The community of people with invisible disabilities remain invisible until other tools are used to spread awareness.

Communication has been my tool to express my conditions and symptoms to others. I'm motivated to share my own experiences to pave the path for others to feel heard and understood when they choose to speak their story. I use communication not only as a way to gain the support I need to thrive, but also to raise awareness for invisible disabilities

---

4   "Invisible Disabilities: List & General Information," Disabled World, updated September 10, 2020.

and the stigmas surrounding them and the people who have them. Each conversation, email, and now book I write helps to explain my experiences to others without being able to physically show them. These discussions also uncover just how many people, especially younger people from adolescence to early adulthood, are grappling with invisible physical and mental disabilities. I look forward to sharing what I've learned from each interaction with those with invisible disabilities who are looking for guidance in their personal, academic, and early professional lives.

Since I've struggled with my conditions from a young age, I've had years to reflect upon the communication process that has worked so well for me. I refer to these dialogues or exchanges as "invisible conversations," a discussion in which I share my invisible disabilities with those around me. Some conversations are easier than others, as I have received a variety of reactions, ranging from deep sympathy to outright denial.

Nonetheless, the many interactions I've had since have caused me to notice a pattern of something I call "positive curiosity." Positive curiosity describes a perspective in which someone who is near to me is naturally concerned for my health and well-being because of their care for me as a person. Those who are positively curious about my conditions help me to feel comfortable enough to show my vulnerabilities and disclose the difficulties my disabilities may cause me. Over time, I've refined these concepts to help me reflect on sixteen-years' worth of discussions I've had from grade school to the end of college, as well as to help prepare me for the conversations I will begin as I enter the workforce. I'm hopeful that by sharing my tactics for holding these invisible conversations, young people with invisible disabilities will feel empowered to start their own.

With practice, sharing my conditions has become easier over time. I've accepted my disabilities are just another part of my identity, though this may not be the case for others with visible and invisible disabilities. While my physical and mental conditions cannot be detected by simply looking at me, they have shaped the person I am inside and the personality I exude to others.

The start of spring semester in my freshman year was my second try toward my bright future; this time, my disabilities would be part of the journey. I still hold my breath when I share my conditions and experiences with others, as a small part of me is fearful of the implications of revealing this part of myself and my identity. But over time, my confidence manages to shine through each interaction, through disabilities and all.

By utilizing the power of invisible conversations with the positively curious people around me, I've learned this new identity that has formed from my past and present can still propel me toward the bright future I've always envisioned. I now look forward to sharing my experiences and the lessons I've learned to help others who have walked a similar path.

CHAPTER 1

SPEAKING WITH YOUR DOCTOR

Growing up, I was a relatively active child. Around seven or eight, I tried almost every sport my town offered for at least a day. My attempts at soccer, gymnastics, and cheerleading never really worked out. I enjoyed playing tennis with my mom, but there were no teams or lessons for children my age. Since I couldn't really stick to a sport, I joined my mom on her daily morning walks.

We'd wake up early in the morning during the spring and summer seasons before the start of school and work. We walked all over town, covering a new route almost every day. My mom and I would share stories and laugh with one another, then end our morning routine with our favorite breakfast sandwiches. I loved walking with my mom and enjoyed the feeling of being active, until one day when I felt a dull ache in my lower back.

I was quick to tell my mom about my back ache; I told her everything on our walks and this pain was no exception.

We couldn't figure out what could be causing my pain, and our usual two-mile walks dwindled to a brief stroll around the block. My back pain impacted other parts of my day, regardless of if I was stationary or moving. That's when the slew of doctors' appointments began.

We began with my pediatrician, then moved on to specialists, who all ordered several tests to be conducted to understand the source of my pain. I had MRIs, CT scans, x-rays, and numerous blood tests that revealed nothing about what could be causing my pain. Growing complaints of worsening aches warranted another round of tests in case they missed something the first couple of times.

Just as my mom and I had been upset by the lack of answers in these tests, it seems my doctors were too. Early on in my journey to understand the source of my pain, a number of doctors eventually dismissed it if they couldn't find a cause through any of their diagnostic tests. They thought I could be lying about my pain for attention, or that it was just in my head and therefore wasn't real. Seeing so many physicians in a short period of time, only to receive these explanations, forced me to consider if they were actually right.

I felt confused and frustrated by their responses to my pain: "Your pain isn't real—it's all in your head." "You're not in pain, you're just looking for attention." "Your mind is making this pain up." At such a young age, I couldn't understand what it meant when they said the pain was in my head. I still don't understand what that means. All I knew was that I was hurting all of a sudden and it had only gotten worse, no matter what my mom and I tried to alleviate it. What kind of help was this diagnosis supposed to give me?

Despite my fatigue and increasing anxiety about these tests, my mom continued to search for more doctors, and hopefully more answers. I grew up spending much of my time in waiting rooms instead of school. My pain continued to evolve as I grew and started to impact my shoulders, ankles, and head. I missed several school days due to these symptoms no one could explain.

During the evenings, I was sent to physical therapy for my back pain. I can remember many days of coming home from school, eating a quick dinner, and being driven a half an hour to my physical therapy sessions. I felt anxious and out-of-place at these appointments, as I was the youngest patient by at least forty years. My pain would skyrocket by the time I returned home from these appointments and I couldn't feel any difference in how I felt in the long-term.

Because my pain continued to change all the time, my mom and I were hopeful one day my new symptoms would be recognizable and I could be diagnosed, and eventually find relief. It was many years of doctors' appointments, tests, and uncertain diagnoses, but we never stopped searching for other opinions to understand what I was experiencing.

The many years of doubt from my doctors caused me to develop a sense of distrust toward the doctors I saw. My chronic pain made me feel helpless. At the start of my diagnosis journey, I put all my faith into my medical team to understand what I was going through and tell me how to handle my symptoms. The doctors I relied on to give me some sort of explanation instead told me my pain was my problem. In these cases, I felt my last chance to find some relief was taken away from me, and I was left back where I started.

At the start of my freshman year of high school, I was experiencing persistent back pain, stomach aches, headaches, and sore skin. Random stabs would ripple across my body, dozens of tiny pains each minute. By this point, I had been seeing various specialists for seven years. One morning that year, I woke up and was unable to walk due to excruciating pain in my ankles. Just like before, we found another doctor, except this time this doctor was able to look past my sudden ankle problem and took in my whole experience with pain. She had heard of a rare condition called Amplified Musculoskeletal Pain Syndrome and pointed us to the Children's Hospital of Philadelphia for further guidance.

My eagerness and distrust instantly clashed. On one hand, I was thrilled to hear there were others like me, and our symptoms had a name. On the other, I was concerned this small lead would just bring me back to square one. My distrust remained even when this first clue as to what my diagnosis may be came along. Nonetheless, my mom and I took this idea and ran with it. Thankfully, this lead would turn out to be the first day of my treatment journey.

Just under a year later, I was admitted into the Children's Hospital of Philadelphia's Amplified Musculoskeletal Pain Syndrome ("AMPS") in-patient program. While there, I completed a full day of physical and occupational therapy, broken up by extracurriculars such as psychotherapy, art therapy, music therapy, and aquatic therapy. My physical and occupational therapy sessions pushed me to the brink, bringing my pain to an all-time high. However, the exact point of the program was to "push past the pain." Your pain could not excuse you from completing these exercises and activities.

Because of this, I quickly came to believe my therapists had somehow resented me. I had never felt so much pain but there was nothing I could say to them to express what I was feeling. No matter what I said, I was met with the same response: push past the pain.

As my pain grew, so did the distrust toward my therapists. Their mantra didn't feel different from what so many doctors had told me in the past—that the pain was in my head, that only I could control it, that I should just push past it. I internalized their response as a dislike for me and lack of care. My distrust transformed into fear as I couldn't decipher whether they wanted me to get better or worse.

I believe my feelings toward my therapists were valid but looking back now I almost feel silly to have even felt this fear and distrust in the first place. My therapists showed me the toughest love anyone had ever shown me before. They knew what it would take to get me to feel better, even if I didn't believe in the process myself. On my last day, I realized just how thankful I was for their help during the program. Unlike other doctors, they never denied my pain. They accepted and understood what I was feeling and told me to keep pushing anyway. Because of this, I am almost entirely pain-free after completing the program.

Nearly five years after I completed the program, I was able to connect with Sam, who was also part of the in-patient

AMPS therapy at her local hospital. Given the uniqueness of the program, I had never expected to find anyone who could relate to my experiences, but both Sam and I could relate to one another and our time in the program.

When I described my feelings toward my therapists to Sam, she expressed an understanding I hadn't received before. During our conversation, Sam had joked that the therapists were like robots: they didn't seem to show any emotion or sympathy for the patients. She shared a tactic she tried during the program to get the therapists to open up a little. "I would try to crack jokes just to get them to show they're humans!"

These therapists aren't just human, they're super-human. As I've reflected on my time in the program, I had never met a medical team that cared more for me and my well-being. I experienced a different type of care than I was used to receiving, but I'm eternally grateful for their help either way.

Through the arduous diagnosis process, I was able to come to the understanding that doctors *do* know what they're talking about—but so do I. Also, my mind and body are as much a part of the diagnosis and treatment process as a doctor's opinion. If I don't feel my experiences are treated equally and wholly, then I've learned to move on and find additional opinions until I'm satisfied.

My experience in the AMPS program was not only the first step to managing my condition, but also the first step toward fixing my feelings and assumptions toward doctors. The many years of doubt from doctors have taught me how to speak up and demand better care for myself, but no one should have to wait so long to receive proper treatment.

My first piece of advice is to prepare for your appointment.[5] The more details you can provide to the doctor, the closer you'll be to a clear diagnosis. This tip applies to both general care and specialist appointments, no matter how many of each you've been to. Consider journaling the following information about your symptom(s):

- What your symptom(s) are and what they feel like
  - Jot down some adjectives to describe what the symptom(s) feel like.[6]
  - For example, if you're experiencing back pain, what does the pain feel like? Is it aching, stabbing, or throbbing? Think of some scenarios to describe what the pain mimics.
- When you first felt your symptom(s), when they occur, and how often they occur
  - It's important to try to find patterns in your symptoms, that way you and your doctor can find some connections between your symptoms and when they occur.
  - Take note of what you're doing when you experience one of your symptoms, paying attention to details such as:
    - What position your body is in
    - If you're being more active or more stationary
- Any recent changes in your routine, diet, exercise, and so on

---

5   "Talking to Your Doctor: How to Make Yourself Heard," WebMD, last modified January 27, 2020.
6   "How and Why to Describe Pain Accurately to Your Doctor," The Ohio State University Wexner Medical Center, November 16, 2018.

Bring this information to the appointment to provide as full of a picture as possible to your physician. While collecting these details, remember to jot down any questions you may have as well. During your appointment, keep taking notes and make sure you've gotten satisfactory answers to your questions; don't be afraid to ask for clarification from the doctor or to insist on getting an answer if a doctor is quick to get out the door. Consider asking the physician for additional time or another appointment over the phone to make sure everything has been covered, saying something such as: "I still have questions about this. Can we make some time to discuss this further?"

Next, if possible, bring someone with you who believes your experiences. They can serve as both moral support and an extra set of ears to help you through this appointment and greater process. During even the hardest appointments in which a doctor outright denies your symptoms and concerns, it can help to have someone besides yourself who believes you.[5] For many years, my mom was my entire support system as she kept pushing for answers in every appointment, subsequently teaching me how to continue the journey for myself.

It's also important to remind yourself that there are countless physicians out there who may be able to help you. Don't be afraid to look for multiple opinions from other doctors and other facilities. Having a full, clear understanding of your symptoms, your diagnosis, and treatment options is important when it comes time to decide which treatment you will pursue.

These diagnosis and treatment journeys can be long, many years long, even for those without invisible disabilities. Do your best to keep your journey documented, including writing your appointments and their outcomes, keeping track of records, and maintaining any outside research or information. At the end of an appointment, read through every page of the packet your doctor may hand to you on your way out of the office, and consider bringing these to your other appointments.

If you are unable to do any of these items, there is one thing you must do above all else: do not doubt yourself or what you're feeling. Your symptoms and experiences are valid, and you should not stop searching for answers until you are satisfied with your care and your treatment plan. I've had to learn my feelings and experiences are just as credible and worthwhile as the doctors' opinions, and if the two are misaligned, then something must be fixed. This could mean having a candid conversation with the physician about my care or finding another doctor altogether. There will many practitioners with many different ideas and beliefs about your conditions, but it's up to you to find the right care that is best for you.

Doctors go through many years of schooling and training, and usually know what they're talking about. But patients, especially younger ones, must ensure their experiences are being weighed equally in the evaluation and diagnosis process. If this is not the case, then patients should feel empowered to seek further information to get the help they need. Your mind and body can know better than anyone else, and you must treat your diagnosis and treatment process as such.

CHAPTER 2

BIAS IN MEDICINE AND HOW IT IMPACTS INVISIBLE DISABILITIES

———

Searching for a diagnosis is no easy feat, no matter what type of condition you may be experiencing. You start experiencing new sensations or symptoms that won't seem to go away. You make an appointment with your general practitioner who likely recommends for you to see a specialist who doesn't have another opening for at least a month. If you've been on the diagnosis path before, you might even bypass your general practitioner and go right to the specialist. On the day of the appointment, you get to explain all of your symptoms to the doctor you hope has the answers. Best case scenario, you have a doctor who listens and sends you off for a round of tests and perhaps some more appointments. Worst-case scenario, your experiences are written off and you're back to square one in your search for an answer.

This quest for a diagnosis is a difficult one. It's even harder for those who may face bias or discrimination from their doctors. Bias in medicine comes in many forms. More studies increasingly seek to understand discrimination in medicine based on sex, gender identity, sexual orientation, race, nationality, age, and more. These aspects of one's identity can get in the way of getting to the bottom of physical or mental health problems, and the obstacle grows when the ailment is not a visible one.

To combat this potential discrimination, I believe knowledge is power. By being aware of the dangers of medical bias, patients will be able to take power into their own hands by recognizing bias when they experience it. I hope with this information, patients will be empowered to speak out against prejudice in medicine during their diagnosis and treatment processes, thus helping to correct the trends of discrimination while working toward a more accurate personal medical plan.

SEX, GENDER IDENTITY, AND SEXUAL ORIENTATION

My gender and my disabilities make up a large part of my identity. I often consider my gender and my disabilities separately, and don't often consider the intersection of the two. I'm a cisgender woman, meaning I identify with the female sex I was assigned at birth, and I have a couple of physical and mental conditions. I face discrimination for both identities, but when combined, the bias mounts. I rarely thought about the intersection of gender and health, and the thought only crossed my mind when visiting doctors for the various problems I've had over the years.

As I grew older, puberty became the scapegoat to blame my pain on. Stomach problems were dismissed as menstrual cramps and bloating. My anxiety was attributed to my womanly sensitivities. It seemed some doctors, who were often cisgender men, struggled to separate my gender from the problems I was experiencing.

As I've grown older, I've begun to attend doctor's appointments by myself, without the support of my mom who was by my side for every appointment since the start of my diagnosis journey. This shift to greater personal responsibility is daunting in many ways, and my gender only made the shift toward greater responsibility harder, as I was subconsciously taught to be wary being alone with men—including doctors.

I'm reminded of a particular experience from my freshman year of college, when I went to one of my first doctor's appointments on my own after sustaining my fourth concussion. I had struggled alone through the process, from the Uber ride to the office, to the waiting room, to the actual appointment. The dense fog I felt around my head wouldn't wane as I waited for the doctor to enter the examination room.

Before leaving me alone in the room, the nurse flicked the fluorescent lights off, giving my pounding head a reprieve. The only light in the room came from the overcast sky, filtered through the window blinds. I lost myself in the view of the gray clouds outside when the door opened soon after and the doctor stepped in. He greeted me with a handshake and retrieved a file from his desk, skimming it over before asking me to re-hash the story of my injury.

I slowly shared my story, from impact to appointment at health services. I mentioned my three other concussions, as well as my AMPS diagnosis. He made no comment as he approached me to begin the examination.

"Pull up your sleeve for me? I'm going to take your blood pressure."

I glanced at my arm and panicked: I failed to plan ahead and chose to wear a tight-fitting button-down flannel to my appointment. I kept pulling, but the sleeve would hardly squeeze past my elbow. He sensed my struggle and came closer to help pull my sleeve up.

"You might have to take your arm out of your sleeve. You can't wear such tight clothes to appointments."

I tensed at his suggestion. I felt my chest clench in panic, my discomfort soaring as I continued to wrestle with my sleeve, willing it to go up further. I tried to reason with the sudden thoughts that flooded my head. *Surely he meant nothing by that. He definitely didn't mean anything by that. I'm just being paranoid.*

No matter the intentions behind the comments, I felt wary of him from that point forward. He agreed to try to take my blood pressure through my sleeve, and fortunately he decided he received an accurate read. The cuff was removed from my arm and I was able to take in a full breath as he stepped away from me.

Throughout the appointment, I went through the motions of the diagnostic tests; drawing cubes, naming animals, and recalling the order of pictures on the page. The sky began to darken as the evening progressed, and the lamp was the last viable source of light in the room. The light was soft on my senses, but the increasing darkness only made my uneasiness worse as I tried to carry on with the rest of the appointment.

There was no overt discrimination or bias in this story, but this experience provided a glimpse into some of the implications of being a woman with pain or a disability. I wonder if the doctor would've said something like this to a young male patient. If so, would he have taken this comment the same way I did? Like many other women, I seek physicians who are also women so I may avoid situations such as this one.

When seeking a diagnosis or treatment, women are often doubted, misdiagnosed, or mistreated. A number of speculations exist as to why this is: women complain more than men; women are not accurate when reporting their pain; men are more stoic when explaining their pain, therefore making it more "real"; and women are able to tolerate pain better than men.[7] So where sdoes this leave women? To go on an endless search for a diagnosis, experiencing bias and error along the way, just to be given a myriad of inaccurate and unhelpful treatments, if granted treatment at all?

On the other hand, while men may not face the same forms of medical discrimination women do, men may struggle to

---

7   Diane Hoffman and Anita Tarzian, "The Girl Who Cried Pain: A Bias Against Women in the Treatment of Pain," *The Journal of Law, Medicine & Ethics* 28, no. 4 (2001): 13-14.

receive the care they need in the first place.[8] Studies have found men are likely to avoid getting yearly check-ups or are dishonest about their medical history or symptoms when speaking with their doctors.[9] This may be due to several causes, such as embarrassment, fear of being judged, fear of receiving a concerning diagnosis, or overall discomfort with discussing their health.[10] Lack of awareness on certain health risks, with conditions such as heart disease, type 2 diabetes, and prostate conditions, also contribute to these complications.[11] By avoiding or delaying appointments, men may be missing out on vital routine screenings that can detect health problems even before they begin to experience symptoms.

This avoidance or silence was also apparent as I searched for stories from men experiencing invisible disabilities. When I invited others to share their stories, only women would respond to my solicitation for an interview. I had to go to much greater lengths to receive responses from men, going so far as to personally message them, and despite this effort, I only managed to obtain a handful of interviews from their perspective.

This health crisis expands to men's mental health, often referred to as a "silent epidemic."[12] Similarly to physical

---

8   Fay Schopen, "The Healthcare Gender Bias: Do Men Get Better Medical Treatment?" *The Guardian*, November 20, 2017.

9   "Why Men Don't Go to the Doctor," AARP, published September 6, 2019, accessed January 18, 2021.

10   Ibid.

11   Ian Banks, "No Man's Land: Men, Illness, and the NHS," *The BMJ* 323, no. 7320 (2001): 1058-1060.

12   John Ogrodniczuk et al., "Men's Mental Health," *Canadian Family Physician Medecin de Famille Canadien* 62, no. 6 (June 2016): 463-464.

health, men are less likely to seek help for depression, substance abuse, and stressful life events due to social stigma, a reluctance to talk about their experiences, and downplaying symptoms.[13] The result of these complications is often deadly, as men die by suicide 3.5 times more often than women.[14] The few men I was able to interview highlighted the importance of mental health awareness, especially when grappling with chronic physical conditions. Phil, one of the few male interviewees, has battled Type 1 Diabetes since 2015. He shared his perspective on managing a disability and your mental health, saying that when you're battling a chronic illness, "... you have no breaks, no vacations, no days off [and that] can be extremely overwhelming."

Other problems mount for non-binary and transgender patients, literally from the first appointment to treatment. Refusal of care, uncertainty about proper treatment due to hormone medication, and overall lack of knowledge on how to treat transgender and non-binary patients are just a couple of the massive problems that keep these patients from getting the care they need.[15] [16] Smaller complications then add insult to injury, such as the lack of training for medical staff on how to address a transgender or non-binary patient when they check in for their appointment.[17]

---

13 "5 Minute Guide to Men's Mental Health," infographic, Mental Health America, accessed January 18, 2021.

14 "A Critical Look at Men's Mental Health," *MindWise Innovations Blog & News* (blog), *MindWise Innovations*, accessed January 18, 2021.

15 Kristin Lam, "Some Americans Are Denied 'Lifesaving' Health Care Because They Are Transgender," *USA Today*, December 11, 2018.

16 Zaria Gorvett, "Why Transgender People Are Ignored by Modern Medicine," *BBC News*, August 16, 2020.

17 Lam, "Some Americans."

Transgender patients who choose to undergo gender confirmation surgery can face issues like these prior to and after their operation. They may struggle with discrimination while pursuing surgery. In some cases, patients may have to obtain permission from multiple physicians before they are permitted to undergo the procedure. Others may continue to face bias after their surgery, as doctors may not be willing or able to treat a transgender patient.[18] Problems such as this span anywhere from primary care, to specialization, to mental counseling services.

Stepping away from sex and gender identity, even more complications related to sexual orientation exist. An example would be the HIV and AIDS epidemic. As the epidemic began and stigma started to mount in the early 1980s, HIV and AIDS were most attributed to men who have sex with other men. In studies conducted by Herek and Capitanio in 1999, they found most heterosexual adults associated AIDS with homosexuality and bisexuality, and those who made that association also tended to harbor a higher level of sexual prejudice than other heterosexuals.[19]

This discrimination not only exists amongst the general public, but also within the medical community. This societal stigma can turn physically dangerous and may lead to severe harm or death, especially within the example of the HIV and AIDS epidemic. The AMA Journal of Ethics lists several reactions healthcare workers may have when interacting with a patient with HIV, including ignoring the patient,

---

18   Ibid.
19   Gregory M. Herek and John P. Capitanio, "AIDS Stigma and Sexual Prejudice," *The American Behavioral Scientist* 42, no. 7 (April 1999): 1130-1147.

providing inadequate care to a patient in pain, refusing to draw blood, or even physically mistreating a patient.[20] This particular study was conducted in the mid-2000s, showing how prevalent this stigma continues to be, despite the additional research and information scientists have gathered. Even outside of the realm of the HIV and AIDS epidemic, patients may experience a variety of obstacles to receiving care, simply due to discrimination on the basis of their sexual orientation.

As if receiving proper care wasn't enough of a struggle because of one's sex, gender identity, or sexual orientation, the diagnosis and treatment process can become even more complicated if you're searching for answers about an invisible disability or illness.

RACE AND NATIONALITY

To put it simply, racial and ethnic minorities do not receive the same level of care as their white counterparts. The history of bias, discrimination, and outright medical abuse stems from centuries ago, in which racial minorities were used for medical experimentation for treatments intended for white people.[21] This bias continues to remain prevalent to this day, as racial stereotypes that exist in the public permeate medical settings and can impact the type of treatment people of color receive for pain or illness.

---

20 Bebe J. Anderson, "HIV Stigma and Discrimination Persist, Even in Health Care," *AMA Journal of Ethics* 11, no. 12 (December 2009): 998-1001.

21 Lily Rothman, "The Disturbing History of African-Americans and Medical Research Goes Beyond Henrietta Lacks," *Time*, April 21, 2017.

Unfounded beliefs such as the idea that the bodies of those who are Black are more resistant to pain than the bodies of those who are white result in disparities in treatment solely depending on one's skin color. A 2005 report from the National Academy of Medicine found "racial and ethnic minorities receive lower-quality health care than white people—even when insurance status, income, age, and severity of conditions are comparable."[22] This perpetuating bias has caused minority communities to experience a higher level of distrust toward medical personnel as compared to white patients.[23] These mounting problems result in higher rates of sickness and mortality for patients of color.

A note from the Harvard Health Blog recounts a story of a Black woman who believed she did not receive proper care due to her skin color. She was experiencing pain from a medical condition and visited her local emergency room to receive treatment. She explained her experience with the medical personnel as they didn't even treat her pain: "They treated me like I was trying to play them, like I was just trying to get pain meds out of them. They didn't try to make any diagnosis or help me at all. They couldn't get rid of me fast enough."[24]

Her medical history gave no indication she was seeking pain pills or that she was there for any other reason besides

---

22 "Implicit Bias and Racial Disparities in Health Care," American Bar Association, accessed January 18, 2021.

23 Katrina Armstrong et al., "Racial/Ethnic Differences in Physician Distrust in the United States," *American Journal of Public Health* 97, no. 7 (July 2007): 1283-1289.

24 Monique Tello. "Racism and Discrimination in Health Care: Providers and Patients," *Harvard Health Blog* (blog), *Harvard Health Publishing*, January 16, 2017.

to receive care for her pain. Fortunately, she was able to receive care elsewhere, but this is often not the case for others. Minorities experience higher rates of misdiagnosis and treatment for physical and mental ailments, if they are granted treatment at all.[25] By removing other variables, such as differences in income, age, and severity of the condition, the underlying and subconscious biases are clear. However, these other variables cannot always be removed as events like the COVID-19 pandemic have exposed the inequities between white patients and patients of color, as the disease disproportionately kills people of color.[26] This bias becomes an even larger hurdle when attempting to diagnose an invisible disability or condition, as some symptoms cannot be proven by examinations and tests. Implicit bias fuels a feedback loop of misdiagnosis, mistreatment, distrust, and so on, thus hurting patients of color in numerous ways.

AGE

Whenever I've heard the word *ageism* in any setting, the term is used to describe discrimination against older adults. The internet has no shortage of articles, resources, and studies about ageism against older generations. However, the definition of ageism itself encapsulates much more, as it describes the "prejudice or discrimination on the grounds of a person's

25 Kelly M. Hoffman el al., "Racial Bias in Pain Assessment and Treatment Recommendations, and False Beliefs about Biological Differences between Blacks and Whites," *Proceedings of the National Academies of Sciences* 113, no. 6 (April 2016): 4296-4301.

26 Sandra Simons, "ER Goddess: COVID-19 Lays Bare Racial Bias in Health Care," *Emergency Medicine News* 42, no. 7 (July 2020): 1, 34.

age."[27] No defined limits or suggestions exist for what age group may experience ageism.

However, when you research ageism in medicine, you'll likely find most results to be surrounding seniors and geriatric care. You can find studies and stories of verbal and physical elder abuse as well as subconscious bias against older populations. One of the most exclusionary definitions of ageism that stuck out to me was provided by Dr. Robert N. Butler: "[ageism is] systematic stereotyping and discrimination against people because they are old."[28] I'm sure he meant nothing by this limited definition, but it is indicative of this broader issue, nonetheless.

Clearly ageism against older adults is likely the larger issue, as older people are often treated poorly or discriminated against by the general public as well as medical personnel simply due to their age.[29] However, I find this definition and narrow view of only including older adults under the definition of medical ageism as, well, ageist! Even if medical ageism against children, adolescents, and young adults isn't as prevalent as the discrimination against older adults, ignoring these cases can be incredibly harmful to younger patients.

This is another aspect of my identity that has served to be an obstacle for diagnosis and treatment. Others tend to assume if you're young, then you should be healthy. This assumption

---

27 *Fowler's Dictionary of Modern English Usage*, s.v. "ageism," accessed January 21, 2021.

28 Regis College, "Why Ageism in Health Care Is a Growing Concern," *Online Degrees* (blog), *Regis College*, accessed January 19, 2021.

29 Ibid.

was also widespread in the doctor's office, as a number of my physicians would assume since I was young and they couldn't physically see anything "wrong" with me, then I wasn't in need of care. At this point I was likely to be told my pain or my symptoms were "in my head," and nothing was physically amiss.

Predicaments such as this can cause delays in diagnosis and treatment for serious medical conditions. During my research I spoke with Stephanie, the daughter of one of my mom's close friends. When I first began my search for stories from others with invisible disabilities, my mom suggested reaching out to Stephanie to speak with her about her conditions. As we spoke, Stephanie highlighted similar difficulties with her doctors as she is seeking an official Lupus diagnosis. As she explains, most of her specialists have diagnosed her with Lupus; she has experienced nearly all of the known symptoms and has a family medical history of Lupus on her father's side. However, her rheumatologist, the only specialist that can diagnose her, refuses to give her this Lupus diagnosis because he believes she is too young. This has caused immense delays in her treatment as she is now currently seeking another rheumatologist.

I also investigated what bias younger children may be experiencing when they and their caregiver are searching for a diagnosis or explanation for new symptoms. Just as I found little to no mentions of medical ageism against adolescents and young adults, few examples or studies surfaced to discuss bias children may face. To understand this better, I spoke with Dr. Susan Honeyman, a professor of English at University of Nebraska-Kearney and lifelong migraine sufferer. Dr. Honeyman has authored a few books. One of her works, *Child Pain, Migraine, and Invisible Disability*, explores how pain in children has been overlooked by adults and doctors who believe the child may be lying about or exaggerating their pain. While she examines this phenomenon through the lens of childhood migraines, her lessons and findings remain true for others experiencing pain or an invisible disability.

She explained to me, "Children are likely to be quieter rather than crying or 'acting out' [when in pain]. Unfortunately, a still and silent child is behaving in a way that actually pleases many adults, so this recoiling from pain isn't recognized as an actual symptom."

Since adults are searching for some sort of adverse behavior to express pain, a child's pain can go unnoticed, undiagnosed, and untreated. Even further, if a child does speak up about pain or discomfort, they are likely to be doubted due to the bias that somehow children are unable to accurately depict their pain or symptoms.

Dr. Honeyman spoke out against this prejudice, and was even able to make ties between her research and her personal experiences with her own physician: "The research cited in my book certainly indicates that children are pretty reliable at reporting and assessing pain and other invisible symptoms, but the bias against recognizing this is so pernicious, that, for example, my own neurologist, upon hearing that I was writing about children with migraine, immediately asked, 'but how do you know if they are telling the truth?' This should never be the first question that a health professional asks about a child's complaints."[30]

This bias against children, so early on in their lives and in their health journeys, can be permanently damaging. If children face a pattern of being doubted, they may lack willingness and ability to advocate for themselves later in life when their problems persist or if other issues occur.[31] It is clear how a history of distrust may persist from this predicament, especially as they become young adults.

Though the problems shift for each age group, the themes and effects of medical ageism against children, adolescents, and young adults is clear. A child's pain journey may begin with the child being doubted or referred to as a liar by healthcare workers, then shifts into another form of doubt as physicians may proclaim this person is too young to be unhealthy or ill. The first step to fighting this prejudice is widening society's and medicine's view of medical ageism to include younger populations.

INTERSECTIONALITY

Each portion of our identity does not always exist independently of other aspects. The more boxes we check on the list of identities or social categories, the more problems may arise when attempting to seek medical care. Intersectionality

---

30 E.F. James, "An Interview with Susan E. Honeyman, Author of: Child Pain, Migraine and Invisible Disability (Routledge 2018)," *Farah Mendlesohn* (blog), *Farah Mendlesohn*, March 14, 2019.

31 "What to Do If a Child Reveals Abuse," Reporting Abuse, accessed February 25, 2021.

can help us to understand the interconnections between our identities and the impact they have on our lives.

Intersectionality is defined as the interconnected nature of social categorizations such as race, class, and gender as they apply to a given individual or group, regarded as creating overlapping and interdependent systems of discrimination or disadvantage. Kimberlé Crenshaw, an American lawyer and civil rights advocate, coined the term in 1989 to describe the point in which our individual characteristics intersect.[32] You can picture a Venn diagram, and each circle serves as an identity or social categorization. The overlap between identities is the intersectionality of a person. Most commonly, a Venn diagram of intersectionality will include race, sexual orientation, gender identity, nationality, and disability. However, keep in mind *many* identities or traits can stem from these, causing the diagram to grow.

People with disabilities already check one of the identity boxes. Once any other box is checked, then an intersectionality develops. One's intersectionality can have an impact on their lives, both positive and negative. Consider myself as an example: I have a couple of physical and mental disabilities. I am also a woman. As detailed in the previous section on sex, gender identity, and sexual orientation, women with disabilities or pain are treated differently than others in a variety of settings. When people learn of my disabilities, some have simultaneously commented on both my disability and my gender identity, such as telling me, "you're too pretty to be sick."

---

32   Jane Coaston, "The Intersectionality Wars," *Vox*, May 28, 2019.

Consider the example of the woman from the section on race and nationality who was Black and did not receive care. She too is a woman with pain or a disability, but her race impacted the type of care she received from others. Other examples work the same way with gender identity, sexual orientation, nationality, and so on.

Because our identities do not often exist independently of one another, they must all be acknowledged and recognized when working along a path to diagnosis and treatment for physical and mental ailments. To be cognizant of the bias against a siloed identity is not enough; the entire person, intersectionalities and all, must be considered when caring for people with disabilities within and outside of medical settings.

Potential complications caused by parts of your identity and intersectionalities make it that much more important to ensure you are receiving proper care from your healthcare team. The first step is to be aware of the biases a physician may intentionally or unintentionally hold against you during your diagnosis and treatment process. By being informed, you will be able to recognize discrimination much faster, allowing you to determine whether or not it is necessary to seek care elsewhere. Regardless of your identities and characteristics, your symptoms and experiences are valid; don't be afraid to keep looking for a doctor who recognizes this fact.

CHAPTER 3

MENTAL ILLNESSES AS INVISIBLE DISABILITIES

———

After sustaining my fourth concussion, I was referred to a physical therapist near my campus. On the day of my appointment, I followed the physical therapist down the stark white hallway, struggling to keep up with her pace as I squinted my eyes so tightly they were nearly closed. She brought me to a dark room on the right side of the hall and invited me inside. The afternoon sun glowed behind the closed blinds of the double windows, providing just enough light inside the room to cast a shadow beneath the examination table and various exercise tools scattered throughout the room.

"Have a seat on the table. I'll be right back to start our in-take examination," she said as she softly shut the door behind her.

"Okay, thank you," I verbalized, unable to nod my head without giving myself a dizzy spell.

My gaze focused on the linoleum floor that was speckled with colorful spots. Unaware of how much time had passed, I stared at the red dot on the tile in front of me until the therapist stepped back into the room and pulled up a seat in front of me. "Alright, let's get started then. I have your file from your appointment with Dr. Graham but go ahead and tell me again what happened and what you're feeling."

My line of sight scanned for other spots on the floor as I inhaled deeply before beginning.

"I was in class when a crutch fell behind me and hit me in the back of the head." I lifted my hand to graze the back left side of my head.

"My eyes got drowsy, and I felt a fog around my head. I haven't been able to pay attention to things going on around me or remember what happened earlier in the day or week."

I continued, "These are the same symptoms I felt during my other concussions, but I feel so much more lost this time around. Even though I can't pay attention to what's happening around me, I'm hyper-aware of things hanging above my head or being thrown near me. I'm moving a lot slower and much more cautiously, like I'm paranoid."

In fact, I had never struggled mentally more than at that point. I avoided leaving my college dorm room as much as I could as I felt a constant fear I could be hit again.

Content with my responses, she turned to the counter-top behind her, grabbing some examination tools. "I'm just going to do a few tests with you to see how you respond," she explained.

I followed her instructions with ease as I had completed the same tests so many times before. My eyes strained to follow the tip of her finger and I struggled to tap my fingers together against my thumb. I could feel just how sluggish I had become as I continued through each exercise.

"Alright, now we're going to try something a little bit different. I'm going to place my hands around your head and quickly jolt your head to the side a few times, okay?" she asked.

Instantly, I felt my body recoil away from her, panicked by her explanation. I brought my arms close to my body and leaned back, attempting to distance myself as my entire form clenched in fear. "I don't think I'm comfortable with that," I timidly tried to explain to her. Alarm bells rang in my head at the suggestion as my gut willed me to outright refuse the exercise, but in my hazy state, I struggled to express my resistance.

She leaned in closer, stretching her arms out toward me. "I know, I'll try to be as gentle as I can." She spoke quickly as she raised her hands to cup the back of my head. When she tightened her grasp, I whimpered and felt the tears well up in my eyes. I felt as though I was dangling on the edge of a precipice, trapped by the hands that gripped my head and my mind.

Without notice, the therapist jerked my head to the left and I was pushed off the edge, sent flying into an intense panic attack. I cried out as I instantly began sobbing, causing her to quickly withdraw her hands. I shook uncontrollably and replaced her hands with my own, cradling my head as I gasped for breath. I hadn't felt any pain or physical discomfort from her actions; my reaction was purely emotional and mental. The therapist urged me to lie down as my sobs grew quieter, retrieving an ice pack to put under my head. Within a few minutes, I managed to calm myself down as she stood to the side, seemingly unsure of what to do with me. She offered me as much time as I needed to lie there and recover from the event, quietly slipping out of the room for the next half hour.

After this appointment I decided I would go home for the rest of my freshman fall semester to restart my recovery that had just been erased. I felt I lacked the mental stability to be able to continue to care for myself, so going home felt like the only option for me to be able to improve.

After weeks of being home and attending several doctors' appointments, I was diagnosed with minor post-traumatic stress disorder. All of my other concussions had been debilitating physically and mentally, but this fourth injury felt like the final straw for my mental health. I suppose I was so jarred and desperately disappointed from my previous injuries that this one sent me into a tailspin.

While my baseline levels of stress and anxiety had contributed greatly to my pain, struggles with my mental health had never been more apparent than they were now with this diagnosis. All my life, I had considered my chronic pain as my greatest struggle, and I somehow neglected the battle that

was going on inside my head, further fuel-
ing my pain. My PTSD diagnosis pushed
me to reflect on the meaning of invisible
disabilities.

The term "invisible disability" can serve as a label for a variety
of conditions that are not identifiable by simply looking at
someone. There are no hints such as a braces, canes, service
dogs, and so on. The meaning of the term changes depending on who you ask and in what context. One of the clearer
definitions is provided by the Invisible Disabilities Association, which includes symptoms of debilitating pain, fatigue,
dizziness, cognitive dysfunctions, brain injuries, learning
differences, mental health disorders, and hearing and vision
impairments.[33]

Raising awareness for invisible disabilities of any type can
help raise awareness for *all* types of invisible disabilities—
physical, mental, neurological, or otherwise. Regardless, it
is important to validate each categorization of invisible disability. In addition, more than one type of invisible condition
can occur in one person, forcing them to focus on multiple
illnesses at once.

The scenario I've witnessed most in my life is a physical disability that causes or has implications with a mental disability. Physical illnesses can cause great mental distress, to the
point where one may be diagnosed with one or more mental

---

33   "What Is an Invisible Disability?" Invisible Disability Association,
     accessed January 21, 2021.

disorders. Consider fibromyalgia as an example, which is most often characterized by widespread pain, fatigue, and cognitive difficulties.[34] The symptoms and diagnosis and treatment processes for fibromyalgia can cause physical, mental, and social distress within a person. Studies estimate about 20 percent of fibromyalgia patients are diagnosed with depression or an anxiety disorder, sometimes as a result of the symptoms they are experiencing.[35] These additional diagnoses require treatment for each condition individually and as a system as a whole.

All of these conditions, physical, mental, neurological, and so on, fall under the umbrella of the invisible disability term, and each is worthy of equal attention and care. For those who are less familiar with the term, invisible disability is assumed to only refer to mental health illnesses. While mental health disorders are not the only type of invisible disabilities, they make up a substantial portion of the invisible disability types.

Before I did more personal research, I struggled to juggle both my physical invisible disability and my psychiatric disabilities. I felt my physical and mental disabilities were just one big invisible disability that could be treated with a single solution. Because of this subconscious grouping of my physical and mental ailments, I found it difficult to consider each condition by itself.

To the best of my knowledge, and the knowledge of AMPS specialists, my particular form of Amplified Musculoskeletal

---

34 "Fibromyalgia," Mayo Clinic, accessed January 21, 2021.
35 "Fibromyalgia," Anxiety and Depression Association of America, accessed January 21, 2021.

Pain Syndrome was caused and continues to be fueled by high levels of stress and anxiety. This tension would cause my pain and discomfort to grow as my worries did. For a long time, I considered anxiety as yet another symptom of AMPS, simply because of how closely stress and pain are tied together.

I did not seek out mental help to understand each portion of my conditions until I was a teenager. Due to this PTSD diagnosis, I once again sought mental help to understand each portion of my conditions. About a year before my AMPS diagnosis, I was also diagnosed with generalized anxiety disorder and depression. At this time, my invisible disability turned into disabili*ties*, and I suddenly had more than one condition on my plate to understand and treat; my new diagnosis was another reminder of the many conditions I was grappling with. While initially overwhelming, I feel by separating my conditions and naming each of them, I was more capable of treating each one. I was intrigued to find out if others had been approaching their conditions in a similar way.

Emma and I met during our inpatient treatment for AMPS at Children's Hospital of Philadelphia in 2014. When we recounted our experiences with our condition and our mental health, our stories were nearly identical. Emma's pain journey began at ten years old. She developed pain in her left ankle, originally thought to be caused by a soccer injury, that worsened and spread throughout both legs as she and her family sought answers to explain her sudden discomfort. Nearly five years later, she received her AMPS diagnosis from the specialists at Children's Hospital of Philadelphia and was approved to participate in the treatment program.

Emma and I are of the same age and were the only two inpatients in the program at the time, so we developed a close bond for the two weeks we were in the hospital. Like me, she had also battled AMPS and anxiety for many years of her life but struggled to separate the two conditions. "I knew pretty early on in my diagnosis and treatment process the anxiety I was experiencing was probably amplified by my condition, but [also knew] it wasn't caused by it."

Despite whether or not someone has any preexisting health conditions, stress and anxiety play a role in every person's health and well-being. In many conditions, such as heart disease, Alzheimer's disease, and AMPS, stress can make an incredible impact.[36] [37] Stress can be attributed to increasing the risk of becoming ill or worsening these preexisting conditions, and subsequent mental health problems, like anxiety, can be difficult to address individually.

AMPS can make separating physical and mental health a difficult task. Since pain, discomfort, and fatigue are often attributed to anxiety, the symptoms of both AMPS and anxiety can play into one another and cause an endless cycle. Emma understood the dynamic between her pain and her anxiety and believed her anxiety wasn't a result of her pain. Despite this personal acknowledgment and belief, she struggled to express this to others around her, including medical professionals.

---

36 "10 Health Problems Related to Stress That You Can Fix," WebMD, last modified April 1, 2014.

37 Children's Hospital of Philadelphia, "Amplified Musculoskeletal Pain Syndrome (AMPS)."

"When I went to the Children's Hospital of Philadelphia for my treatment, I tried to explain the anxiety I was feeling, but felt the therapist [had] kind of dismissed it by saying it was normal for someone with AMPS to experience anxiety." This feeling of dismissal was familiar to me as well, as I was reminded of the numerous times my own experiences and beliefs were ousted by doctors. I hadn't experienced the same dismissal during the AMPS program, but it was easy to resonate with Emma's recollection.

I also spoke with Stephanie, who is seeking an official Lupus diagnosis. She has experienced symptoms since at least ten or eleven years old. She bounced between public school and homeschooling for years as her body pain and migraines became more severe, and she developed a couple of kidney infections. Now, as she nears her early thirties, she continues to grapple with issues such as sensitivity to sunlight and worsened eyesight.

Stephanie has grown frustrated over time when visiting new doctors as she feels no one will sit down and simply listen to her experiences. Similar to Emma's experience, Stephanie would share her symptoms and experiences, then be dismissed by the doctors she had visited. While Stephanie's symptoms had mostly been physical, she too recognized the role mental health has played in her condition and treatment.

Stephanie has, with or without the support of her doctors, taken it upon herself to try to recognize her symptoms and her triggers. Her mental well-being is a major consideration to get to the bottom of her symptoms. Stephanie shared her struggle with depression and how her depressive episodes can increase the pain she feels as a result of her Lupus.

"I have found that in my really bad depression swings, I can tend to be in much more physical pain and then I will get so depressed because I'm in so much pain, but I end up realizing part of the pain is because I'm depressed," she explained.

The cycle of physical and mental health continues as a result, and it can spin out of control before you are able to get a handle on what is actually wrong. For Stephanie, the trick is to figure out what the cause is and differentiate what is going on in your body and mind. When determining this, she considers what may be causing some mental turmoil, like being on social media too much, too much exposure to the news, or feeling like the world is at an all-time low from all the content around us. By reflecting on this, she can change her habits to reduce her anxiety and depression, thus reducing the pain caused by her low mental well-being. Reflecting on past experiences and symptoms allows you to understand how certain things make you feel both physically and mentally, thus helping you to avoid these triggers. Since becoming aware of my mental well-being, I've used my own reflections and personal insights to inform others about what may cause me physical or mental discomfort, such as certain physical activities or being near flying objects around my head.

Stephanie shared her own reflection she's tried to implement in her own life. "If what you're doing every day is not helping your anxiety, then you need to change [your habits]. The first change is going to make you even more anxious, but if you find yourself feeling better after about a week or so, then you'll realize your mental state was not as great as you thought it was before you changed your habits."

Stephanie believes people with invisible disabilities must be highly aware of their mental health. By being able to check in with yourself, both physically and mentally, you may be able to find the source of your pain or discomfort, allowing you to tend to your symptoms better.

Emma concluded her story with a similar sentiment. Her best advice to others with physical invisible disabilities is to care for both your physical and mental health. You can tend to your mental health in a number of ways, such as attending therapy, exercising and eating well, or simply sharing your experiences with someone supportive.[38] Emma states that seeing a therapist after her treatment significantly allowed her to stay pain free and manage any lingering symptoms of both AMPS and anxiety.

By seeking additional perspectives, I was able to understand how others can juggle their physical and mental conditions and what tricks work for them when managing their disabilities. Not only does their advice apply to their groupings of illnesses, but it can also be applied to individual conditions. Both have provided helpful tips in managing mental health, which has become an increasing issue around the world, especially in younger populations.

As mentioned earlier, invisible disabilities are becoming more prevalent in young adults, particularly in the mental

---

38 "How to Look after Your Mental Health," Mental Health Foundation, accessed January 21, 2021.

health disorder category. One in ten Americans are estimated to have a medical condition that could be considered an invisible disability.[39] Breaking this number down further, the Americans with Disabilities Act states that people with psychiatric disabilities make up a large percentage of total invisible disabilities.

This large percentage is also apparent in younger people, as invisible disabilities are the most common type of disability amongst college students. The National Institute of Mental Health estimates more than one in four young adults between the ages of eighteen and twenty-four have a diagnosable mental illness.[40] Reported symptoms of mental illness from college students have increased by 14 percent over the past decade, and the problem doesn't seem to be slowing.[41]

One potential cause of the rise in mental illness symptoms in young people is the increased use of technology and social media. Coincidentally enough, Stephanie had mentioned the impact social media can have on her mental health, and therefore, her physical health.

Stephanie sought support for Lupus in various Facebook groups. She was looking for positive reinforcement and motivation from others to push past her symptoms, but instead she felt mentally drained from reading about the experiences

39   Disabled World, "Invisible Disabilities."
40   "Mental Illness," Statistics, National Institute of Mental Health, last modified January, 2021.
41   Emily G. Lattie, Sarah Ketchen Lipson, and Daniel Eisenberg, "Technology and College Student Mental Health: Challenges and Opportunities," *Frontiers in Psychiatry* 10, no. 246 (April 2019): 1-5.

of others. "People seem to want to play this victim complex and focus on their limitations, but I'm looking for support to look past my limitations...I don't want to take away from people's experiences, but I'm not getting the support I need."

Stephanie felt herself being dragged down by the negative outlooks she discovered in these online groups. Like many others, her mental health majorly impacts her physical health, so she made the decision to stay out of the groups to maintain her mental well-being. Now, she attempts to find support from specific individuals with similar aspirations and life goals as herself, simultaneously taking her mind off of her condition while also encouraging her toward her goals. Stephanie's example is just one small part of the impact social media and technology can have on mental health.

It's important to note the impact of social media, internet, and technology isn't all negative. In recent years, countless blogs, organizations, and other resources have emerged with the goal of helping those struggling with their mental health, whether it be a short-term or more chronic issue. This increased accessibility for resources allows people to find and experiment with a few solutions to find what tips work best for them.

A simple search on the internet or on social media will result in a slew of resources and tips on how to bolster your mental health, during short-term and long-term struggles.[42] Eating well, exercising, and meditating are often at the top of the list;

---

42 "31 Tips to Boost Your Mental Health," Mental Health America, accessed January 21, 2021.

at my lowest points, these tactics can be incredibly daunting, and I feel incapable of trying them. I've done my best to integrate these practices into my daily life, but I have also kept other techniques in the back of my head when I need a more immediate fix.

Many of these activities either revolve around taking some time for yourself to reflect and recollect yourself, while others recommend using communication, in the form of conversations and writings, to reach out to others for support.

To re-center myself, I enjoy coloring, dancing, and listening to music. I'll poke around on YouTube to find a video from some of my favorite accounts. When I'm feeling more introspective, I may write a page or two of creative writing based on my thoughts. I'm not always able to pull myself out of my rut. When I've got something on my mind I need to share, I often share my thoughts with those closest to me. I also try to spend time around others, whether it be with friends or in a bustling location.

Meditating and speaking with a therapist provide me with a longer-term solution, as I'm able to improve my mental health over time. Additionally, I set a handful of goals for myself for the day, week, month, and year. While these may not be directly tied to my mental health, these goals can help me remain focused on working toward something better than where I am now. I also look to others for a positive influence and work hard to surround myself with others who support me and focus on the brighter things in life. I've recently joined Instagram and often look for new accounts from people who are like me and that I can resonate with.

I didn't find these exercises overnight. It took a long time to figure out what worked best for me to cope with my depression, anxiety, and post-traumatic stress disorder. I also don't use the same tactics all the time or at the same frequency, as my needs may change depending upon how I'm feeling over time. When I struggled to find the right coping mechanisms for me, I thought I was doing something wrong and wasn't trying hard enough to lift myself back up once again.

However, I've learned you need to experiment with different ideas and activities. You can research endless resources and find countless recommendations from others around you, but it is up to you to understand what will work best for you and your situation. When I first began my search for help, I struggled to accept some advice from others, and refused to try their ideas. I gave the excuse that they didn't understand my experiences and what I needed to feel better; in actuality, I didn't understand what I needed either. It's important to keep an open mind and give new people or ideas the benefit of the doubt. You'll never know unless you try!

The same practices won't work for everyone. For example, we'll revisit the good and bad sides of social media. Through my new Instagram account, I've been searching for the positive parts of these platforms, while being mindful of the negative aspects. I've found dozens of accounts from people like me who document and share their experiences with their conditions, and it can reduce the feelings of isolation that can come with disabilities. However, I'm careful to not scroll too long, as some content can reinforce feelings of frustration and hopelessness. I've learned to use this resource in moderation.

Both individual and combined invisible disability types are impacted by internal and external factors. When juggling more than one type, you must be cognizant of the cycle of symptoms that has the potential to quickly spin out of control. The cycle of physical and mental invisible disabilities serves as a strong example of the influence one condition can have over others, and vice versa.

By recognizing the cycle, the lesson has come full circle, understanding the influence mental health can have on physical health: by tending to the cause and symptoms of one's stress or anxiety, the positive effects can be clear in one's physical well-being. In summation, physical and mental illnesses must be treated individually and as a whole. By getting to the root of each condition, the cycle between physical and mental symptoms may be able to be stopped before it grows out of control.

CHAPTER 4

TALKING WITH PARENTS & FAMILY MEMBERS

———

Halfway through my arduous day of endless exercises, I made a quick retreat to my hospital room. My fifteen-year-old feet carried me through the long hallway, waiting room, and wing entrance to the elevator. The doors closed behind me and I paced in the large space, willing the elevator to rise faster. When I exited, my pace evolved into the start of a desperate sprint as I rounded the corner, down the next wing to my room.

My mom sat in a chair at the far end of the room, next to the stand that held my lunch tray. Upon seeing her, the relief spread through my body and I walked into my mom's waiting arms.

"I was so scared you weren't going to be here when I came back."

I heard her scoff softly. "Where was I going to go? We didn't even say goodbye yet."

I gave her a final squeeze before we separated, and I sat down to have my first meal. Between bites, I nervously recounted my day to her. I was scared to glance at the clock too much as I cringed at every movement of the second hand.

A half an hour passed by as I took a final bite of my apple. My eyes met my mom's as a nurse entered through the open door, softly urging me to follow her to my next destination at another part of the hospital.

Over these remaining hours, I was forced to make my body ache all over while completing taxing and tedious physical and occupational therapy exercises. It felt as though I shed a tear for every jolt of pain that coursed through me. Despite all of this, I knew the most painful part of the day would be saying goodbye to my mom hours later.

As I watched my mom's figure slowly disappear behind the closing door, I could still feel the lasting hug she gave me as we whispered our temporary farewells. Even though

I knew she would be there tomorrow and nearly every other day after over the coming weeks, I also knew the isolation that awaited me in my empty room once she left.

I don't think there's a feeling of loneliness quite like sitting in an empty hospital room. The sound of the television can't replace the silence in the room, no matter the volume. The soft light from the bedside lamp leaves dark corners unilluminated. The heat seeping through the ceiling vents barely reaches the icy linoleum floors.

Now that the sun has gone again, the blinds have been drawn back to reveal the midnight blue sky. The tall buildings blend into the darkness and their brightly lit windows serve as twinkling stars in the foggy sky. At night, this is a three-walled room with a gateway to the murky heavens. After the sun goes down, this is a limitless space that juts high into the atmosphere—what an unfortunate place to be alone.

PARENTS

Before you've gained the ability to fully express yourself and your experiences to your doctors, you likely interact with and confide in your parent(s) or guardian(s). Our parents are our first line of defense when something isn't right with our bodies. When seeking medical help, parents serve as a vital messenger between our experiences and symptoms and the doctor.

Parenting is described as the "single largest variable" implicated in scenarios such as childhood illness, childhood development, and mental illness, among others.[43] Any level of involvement, from helicopter parenting to total parental absence, can have a long-lasting impact on a child's future. This impact is amplified when a child develops an illness or disability.

The responsibility of parents in general can be outlined in three parts: protecting a child from harm, defining and enforcing boundaries and rules as a child grows, and supporting their overall development and progression for later in their life.[44] These components can shift in cases in which a child develops a short or long-term health problem. Each parent, guardian, or caregiver decides how to balance these parts in their own parenting approach and as their child's health changes.

Dr. Leora Kuttner is a clinical psychologist who has worked closely with children in pain and their caregivers.[45] Many years of research have proven a child's experience with pain is valid and should be cared for as much as we would

---

43   Masud Hoghughi, "The Importance of Parenting in Child Health," *The BMJ* 316, no. 7144 (May 1998): 1545-1550.

44   Ibid.

45   Jodi Thomas, "Dr. Leora Kuttner: A Pediatric Pain Pioneer and Champion for Kids All Over the World," *The Meg Foundation* (blog), *The Meg Foundation*, October 21, 2020.

an adult's. She spoke about the role caregivers can play when encouraging their child to seek treatment: "What we've seen again and again is that by not empowering children to help themselves or empowering caregivers or clinicians, there's often a deterioration in the child or their willingness to cooperate. There's a loss of confidence to help themselves or a sense of fear or terror that they're going to be hurt and their only way to control the situation is through avoidance."

Responsibility from parent to child shifts as we age through adolescence and early adulthood. As an adult, you must serve as your own organizer and advocate for your care. How you seek that care, if at all, can largely be determined by your caregiver's practices and behaviors. While seeking care for their child, caregivers are also teaching their child how to seek care for themselves.

For most of my life, I have been incredibly close with my mom. While I believe we would still be close without the existence of my pain, I also assume my pain and conditions have brought us even closer. She has been by my side for the better part of my twenty-two years, from the start of my pain and hopefully through the eventual end. Over these many years of appointments, she has served as my role model to understand how to advocate for myself.

My mom made immense sacrifices to take me to appointments, physical therapy, and more. She has spent countless nights rubbing my aching muscles, holding me close until I could drift into sleep. She always believed me and believed the pain I was experiencing was real, and she fueled the search to find out what was ailing me. My mom took on the responsibility of translating my complaints and cries into defining symptoms at doctors' appointments.

I am incredibly fortunate to have a parent who always believed and continues to believe my pain and symptoms. As I've grown, I've come to learn few people experience the same pains I have, and I now realize how difficult it may have been to understand the feelings I was weeping about over the years.

The starkest example is the pain that is caused from my allodynia, which is characterized by pain from a stimuli that doesn't usually cause pain.[46] For many years, I experienced excruciating skin pain. It felt as though my entire body was covered in severe sunburn and was continuously scorched with every touch of the skin. Even my softest clothes would feel like they were burning me. The sensation was like feeling every hair on my body as pain exploded across my skin at the slightest touch.

I would often feel these pains before getting sick. As a child, I recognized the pattern of experiencing achy skin and then becoming ill a few days later; because of this, I used to tout that I knew when I was going to be sick. To anyone who has no idea what this skin pain feels like, you wouldn't know what I'm trying to describe. For a long time, my mom assumed I was simply complaining of body aches associated with a common cold or flu.

---

46 "Everything You Should Know About Allodynia," Healthline, last modified August 21, 2018.

But as I grew and learned how to better describe my symptoms, I was able to better express that these pains weren't simple body aches, but instead a searing surface-level burn that had the potential to trigger a severe headache and other symptoms.

During appointments, my mom would take these wild descriptions and her own observations to try to prove to my doctors something was wrong. As discussed earlier on, I often faced bias from doctors because of my age. Even within the medical community, many physicians assumed I was making up this pain to get attention, get out of school or sports, and many other excuses.

My mom and I both experienced desperation and disappointment for the many years we looked for a diagnosis. But it was my mom who helped me keep pushing for an explanation for my symptoms, even when I felt like abandoning the search for answers. I would attribute every bit of pain relief I have felt to my mom and her efforts to find a diagnosis for me.

I've often asked how she felt during this entire process, and most often she replies she was simply frustrated there was nothing she felt she could do to help me. But she has never really expressed her side of the story on my diagnosis and treatment journeys. To learn more about the parent perspective, I spoke with a few parents about the impact their child's condition has had on their lives and the lives of their families.

In one of my interviews, I spoke with Suzanne about her relationship with her nineteen-year-old daughter Isabeau, who began experiencing the start of her symptoms at age four. Isabeau has been diagnosed with AMPS, Postural Orthostatic Tachycardia Syndrome (also known as POTS), and a MTHFR gene mutation. These conditions have left her with chronic full-body pain, anxiety, and depression, among other symptoms.

Suzanne spoke to me about the great lengths she went through to try to provide Isabeau with at least some relief. She listed just a few of the remedies she has bought for her daughter to try out to find some relief.

"I have done everything I can to help her. I've purchased so many items, like weighted blankets, the Quell wearable, numerous different electrolyte powders, essential oils, different nausea remedies, compression socks, orthotics, cooling towel, and on and on to try and help her feel better."

Isabeau is a current college student and lives on-campus about an hour from home. Suzanne recounts how her efforts to help Isabeau's symptoms didn't stop once she went to college: "I worked my butt off to complete all kinds of forms to get her assistance, most recently public money, scholarships, and small loans so she could attend college. I set up infusions in her dorm room. I drive an hour to bring her home for more appointments."

Even through the interview, it was clear how severe of a strain Isabeau's conditions placed on her, her mom, and their relationship. Suzanne shared her frustrations when she feels as though her daughter has the energy to hang out with friends and do the activities she wants to but seems to lack the energy to do chores and help around the house. "I try to put myself in her shoes. I try not to make it about me. But I must do my own self-care and have my own life—maybe detachment is just my way of coping."

This point starts to refer back to one of the three responsibilities a parent bears when caring for their child.[47] It can be difficult for parents and their children to decide on and stick to rules or guidelines for their child when they lead a different life from others their age. With little support or advice from doctors or other parents, one can only hope they are doing what is best for their child given their circumstances.

Suzanne ended this reflection with a bittersweet conclusion: "I adore Isabeau and think she is beautiful, talented, creative and hilarious. But the illness has the upper hand in everything. It is always there in every nook and cranny of our lives."

After this interview with Suzanne, I wanted to understand more about what advice parents share with their children or other caregivers for people with invisible disabilities. Many highlighted their endless search for new treatments, regiments, or products that may have some sort of impact, just like Suzanne had tried.

Others like Denise shared some words of wisdom that had served her and her daughter well when managing her symptoms. Denise taught her daughter the importance of listening to her own body and intuition, or "to go with the gut." She believes by understanding what your body is trying to tell you, it makes you feel as though you have more control

---

47   Hoghughi, "Importance," 1545-1550.

over the situation. As she states, "Giving [your child] some control in an out-of-control situation goes a long way to solve problems."

Throughout my discussions and interviews, I learned the invaluable role parents can play in their children's lives when their child is faced with a disability or pain. Had it not been for my own mom, I likely would've stopped my search for a diagnosis and treatment a long time ago. Now that my conditions have progressed and been in-flux for a few years, I expect I'll have to begin seeing some doctors again to understand what's going on. However, this time around, my mom has taught me how to stand my ground and keep pushing for the diagnosis and treatment that is right for me.

I'm incredibly fortunate to have the relationship I have with my mom, but I recognize others may have to rely more on themselves to effectively share their experiences to find the right treatment. At the end of the day, parents are just one form of support for you in your medical journey. While you look within yourself for strength and determination along your path to diagnosis and treatment, don't be afraid to search for other sources of support from those around you.

FAMILY MEMBERS

When it comes to telling family members about my disabilities, there have been mixed results. This appears to be the same case for those I've interviewed who have invisible disabilities. Out of the ten or so one-on-one interviews I conducted, nearly every person stated they have shared their conditions with their immediate and extended families.

For some, it has been a positive experience: either they receive an outpouring of support from their relatives, or they interact minimally with their family members who aren't impacted by their reactions. Like my relationship with my mom, many interviewees found they were comfortable confiding in and seeking support from their other family members.

I've had some similar interactions with my own family members, many of which my mom has shared my conditions with. I don't get to see my extended family often, but those I do see, such as my godmother, uncles, and aunt, are incredibly supportive and attempt to learn more to understand my conditions. However, given how positive and understanding their reaction is, it seems like some family members and friends only know me for my conditions.

It feels as though the question "how are you?" or "how is Alex doing?" doesn't look for answers regarding school, hobbies, or overall well-being; these questions are looking for a response pertaining to my pain and illnesses. Over the years, as I've treated and learned how to manage my symptoms, these answers have changed. Fortunately, I can share that I've never felt better. Despite these improvements, I still feel like the only thing I am known for to others is that I have a disability.

As far as the explicitly negative interactions with family members and family friends go, I'm fortunate they have not been so unsupportive as compared to other stories I've heard. There has always been a handful of relatives who simply do not understand I have a disability and experience chronic pain. If they're not outright denying my pain, they instead pass on well wishes or attempt to say things they think should make me feel better.

When I interviewed Derek about his condition, he shared a few stories and references like this that I resonated with. In his early thirties, Derek began experiencing unexplained headaches. After a series of appointments and tests over many months, a doctor requested he complete an MRI to "rule some things out." The MRI discovered several lesions on Derek's brain, and it was at this point the doctors considered the possibility of multiple sclerosis.

His doctor requested they complete a follow-up MRI sometime later to determine whether Derek could have Multiple Sclerosis (MS). Six months after the first scan, and a whole year after Derek first began experiencing headaches, the follow-up MRI confirmed Derek's diagnosis for multiple sclerosis.

In our interview, Derek reflected on the time leading up to his diagnosis: "In hindsight I had symptoms, but never put two and two together. I was sore all the time, but I was also training very hard in the gym. I often felt mentally and physically drained after a day of work but at the time I wasn't happy with what I was doing. I did notice my memory getting worse but thought I was just getting old. A lot of dots that never got connected until [my diagnosis]."

Derek also shared his discomfort with telling his family and friends about his journey with MS. "I'd much rather talk to a room full of strangers than my own family. Strangers want to know more; family and friends want to make you feel better...

They all want to tell you how they know someone who has [MS] and that person still goes hiking or runs marathons. Or they tell me how I'm so young and active and I should be fine. Or that they couldn't even tell by looking at me."

At the time of our interview, it had been two years since Derek was diagnosed, and he was able to reflect on some of what he's learned when it comes to sharing your disability with family and friends: "...I've learned how much work goes into making sure people can't tell. People want to invalidate the disease as if minimalizing it or dismissing it entirely makes me feel better about having it. I get they're trying to help, but it's very difficult talking to someone who does not have MS as well."

He also mentioned how much easier it is to speak with someone who has MS so he doesn't have to try to cover up his symptoms and experiences. "I feel the best when I'm talking about my MS and helping others going through the same thing. For that reason, I'll talk to anyone any day about it. People without MS will [gain] a better understanding, and those with it will maybe feel less alone, and hopefully have some insight to help them on their journey living with this illness."

Fortunately, as more resources have become available for people with disabilities, more sources of support for parents and family members of someone with a disability or illness are also being created. Long-term research on childhood development have helped us to better understand the role a parent or family member can play in our care and advancement through each stage of life. For example, Dr.

Kuttner's research on the role parents or caregivers play help us to understand how medical avoidance can develop at a young age and stay with us throughout our lives, and more importantly, how that can be avoided.[48] Articles, blogs, and social media accounts can provide a close perspective for caregivers to find comfort and commonality in.

When it comes to managing and sharing your condition with others, it's up to you how you want to share and how much you'll share, and the same is true for close and extended family members. It's difficult to evade both the positive and/or negative impact a caregiver or family member can have as they are your first support system. Building an understanding and supportive network around you can be crucial to managing a disability or illness, but at the end of the day, it is a personal decision about who you think you can trust to be in that network.

---

48 Thomas, "Dr. Leora Kuttner."

CHAPTER 5

CHANGING HOW YOU SEE YOUR DISABILITY

———

Our parents, caregivers, and doctors are among the first people we can share our pain, discomfort, or other symptoms with. They are also likely to be some of the most understanding people we share our experiences with, as they are among the first to hear when we need help. When we share with our parents and doctors, it's difficult to sugarcoat our complaints and symptoms, as all information is vital to getting a proper diagnosis and treatment.

The people you meet later in life, starting in childhood, will receive the abbreviated version of your condition. These include classmates, friends, teachers, partners, colleagues, employers, and many more. Your decision of whether or not to share your condition with these people in your life, as well as how much you disclose to them, is your own. But unlike your relationship with your caregivers and doctors, immediate understanding and acceptance can be harder to come by when sharing your condition with those you meet later in life.

I've gone through many years of trial and error when telling others around me about my symptoms. When I had first begun to develop pain around seven or eight years old, I thought others my age were experiencing the same; at this age, I couldn't understand why my classmates would give me funny looks or mock my pain after I mentioned it to them. After my diagnosis journey began, it was eventually clear many of my peers could not relate to my pain and tended to make fun of the things they couldn't understand.

As I progressed through each grade and grew older, I went through multiple phases of disclosure. At some points, I felt comfortable opening up to classmates and teachers. Other times, I avoided mentioning my symptoms to anyone besides my mom and doctor, fearful of the ridicule that had begun as I got older. Very few friends knew I was absent all the time because of doctors' appointments and unbearable pain days.

After reaching low points in my health during high school and college, I finally decided for myself that I was better off sharing my conditions with teachers, friends, and classmates. I learned how to share my experiences, as well as how much to share, and when sharing would be most beneficial to me, such as communicating with my teachers and professors at the start of a class. I've learned these lessons through trial and error. After careful reflection, I realize two factors impacted if and how I shared my experiences: how I viewed myself and how I viewed my disabilities.

Like everyone else growing up, I've had my ups and downs about my self-esteem. Unlike others around me, my view of myself was also impacted by my pain and disabilities.

Periods of low self-confidence and anger toward my dysfunctional body caused me to close myself off from others who I assumed wouldn't understand or accept my disabilities. I felt as though I displayed someone other than myself to those around me, while inside of my own head, I was hung up on my disabilities and weaknesses. How I viewed myself and my conditions determined whether I felt safe and secure enough to open up to get the support I needed.

Halfway through high school, I had hit a turning point in which I could no longer carry the weight of my conditions on my own while juggling so much schoolwork and extracurriculars. I was desperate for understanding from teachers and classmates so I could receive accommodations to better fit my schedule that was riddled with absences. I knew I would be in a better position if I reached out for help, as opposed to relying only on myself. By opening up to others through communication, I was able to shift how I thought about myself and my disabilities, a lesson I hope to share with you.

Your disability, condition, or illness does not make you weak. You are not defined by your symptoms or the diagnosis you have received. No matter what others may think or say about you, your experiences, within and beyond your disability, are valid. You are in control of how you respond to your condition and the life you lead. You are the only one who has the power to change your view of all of yourself. You have the power to change it for the better.

Your self-image can impact how you share yourself and your experiences with others. If you're looking for understanding, acceptance, and support from others, you must first find it within yourself for who you are. Only then will you be prepared to open yourself up to others to gain the support you're looking for. You'll always find people who don't believe you or simply don't care about you and your condition but a positive and considerate self-image can motivate you to find the people who will be on your side.

I didn't change my mindset overnight; there were times I could feel myself being dragged down by those who were unaccepting of what I shared with them. But for every little victory where I found a classmate, friend, teacher, or colleague who believed me, my determination to share my experiences to gain the support I desired grew so much more. I invite you to view this evolution in self-image as another journey: through every up and down, stay on the course toward a kinder mindset and self-belief. This transformation in mindset can assist you in finding so many others along the way who can provide the same understanding and support you allow yourself.

CHAPTER 6

POSITIVE CURIOSITY & INVISIBLE CONVERSATIONS

"Is there anything I can do to help?"

When I tell someone close to me about my disabilities, this is the first and most common response I get after explaining my conditions. Such a simple question carries weight and meaning with it, as this person is wondering what they can do to assist me during my times of need. The answer I give varies with each person, as it depends on our type of relationship and how often we interact.

But no matter who it is, I always let others know the best way they can help me is by listening. They have already helped by allowing me to share my experiences and vulnerabilities with them. By doing this, I hope to build an understanding of what's going on when I eventually face periods of lows and try to avoid the pressure of having to explain myself later.

A response like this is something I call positive curiosity—when someone cares about my health, well-being, and is interested in learning more about my predicament and what role they can play in my pain treatment and management. Other examples of positive curiosity include doing their own research into my conditions or checking in on me every so often to see how I'm feeling.

Positive curiosity is characterized by traits such as empathy or sympathy, listening, patience, and interest. It is unlikely someone would be intrigued by physical or mental conditions unless someone they knew and cared for was experiencing one. Because of this compassion for another person, the urge to help them is that much stronger.

Oftentimes, positive curiosity is the factor that influences or determines the types of relationships I have. In these relationships, a safe space exists between myself and the other person. They help me to feel comfortable enough to open up about anything that may be going on when I am ready to share it. Even if I am unable to fully explain what I'm feeling and experiencing from my conditions, they give me the opportunity to come to them for support in nearly any situation, such as an emergency hospital visit.

Typically, this only occurs after communicating with someone about my disabilities. Otherwise, only those who are highly compassionate and cognizant of the emotions or feelings of others tend to express positive curiosity. Since this is often not the case when meeting new people or developing relationships with others in our lives, communication is the first step to developing positive curiosity.

When dealing with invisible physical, mental, or neurological disabilities, what someone sees versus what we feel is different. Without hints of disability such as a wheelchair, brace, or cane, others around us assume there is nothing wrong with our bodies or minds. Since we cannot see invisible disabilities, we need other methods of disclosing our conditions to others. For me, I utilize communication, typically through simple conversation.

I term these conversations of disclosure as "invisible conversations," which refers to a few different things. On one side, it alludes to verbal exchanges about invisible disabilities, including conversations in which I disclose my disabilities to others for the first time, when I mention them in passing, or when I share about a particular experience from my condition. On the other side, the term is symbolic of the intimacy and rarity of these conversations. For many people with disabilities, it takes trust and a feeling of comfort to share their conditions voluntarily and willingly with others. When this disclosure occurs, it is often through one-on-one conversations since a deeply personal experience is being shared.

An example is when I've shared my disabilities with my teachers and professors; I've made the choice to disclose my conditions to them so I can receive accommodations in class when I need them. I could also show how I'm feeling with a friend who knows about my conditions. I may need to reschedule a lunch or change our activity to something I feel more capable and comfortable with at that time because my symptoms flared up. I consider these examples because they are personal conversations about my disabilities between myself and a member of my support system.

Necessary to note is these conversations can take place voluntarily or involuntarily. When I willingly mention my conditions to others, I feel comfortable and safe opening up to this other person. I may feel sharing my condition is necessary to get support or understanding. During these positive dialogues, I've found the person I've spoken with has been happy to do what they can, and we can build a mutually supportive relationship over time.

An involuntary invisible conversation can take place when you feel pressure to share your conditions with others. Usually, an external factor makes you feel obligated to share with those around you. For example, I involuntarily shared my disability with my professors and peers each time I sustained a concussion or had to miss class due to severe pain. When unable to hide my pain or other symptoms, I feel compelled to provide a reason for why my health declines. This can also include partial disclosure of one or multiple conditions; I could feel obligated to mention my pain disorder, but I will not mention the anxiety condition that fuels it. In cases where I'm directly confronted about my symptoms, I may feel pressure to give the antagonizers some information to get them off my case.

In the guide below, I've listed the factors I consider as I decide if or when I disclose my disabilities to someone, and how. These steps are not intended to be followed linearly, as you can determine what considerations to make when it works for you, based on your condition(s).

A GUIDE TO ENGAGING IN INVISIBLE CONVERSATIONS

- Determine what parts or details of your condition(s) you wish to share.
  - Consider if there are any aspects of your condition(s) you would rather not discuss with others. Similarly, consider what details you may have to provide to clearly explain your symptoms and their impact. For example, you will likely have to disclose more to your doctor to receive a better diagnosis and treatment, but you can pick and choose what information to provide when sharing with friends or peers.
  - Consider if who you are speaking to will impact what or how much you share about your condition(s).
- Determine who you will be sharing your condition(s) with and when you plan to speak with them.
  - Consider why you want to share with a specific person. Will they help you receive accommodations at school or work? Do you work with them often or spend a lot of time with them? Do you just want to share these details with someone close to you?
  - When looking for others to be part of your support network, consider speaking with people you believe will display the traits of positive curiosity: attentiveness, patience, and sympathy or empathy.
  - Consider if there is a certain time you need or want to speak with others about your condition(s). For example, if you were to share your condition(s) with your teachers to obtain accommodations for your classes, it would be best to reach out and speak with them before the start of the school year or semester so they may have time to approve and implement your accommodations.

- Think about how the person or people you will have this conversation with will respond.
  - It can be difficult to predict how those around you will respond to your disclosure of your condition(s) and your symptoms. Hopefully, they can offer you understanding and support. However, this isn't always the case. Consider what type of reaction someone may have during this conversation, and perhaps consider planning an alternative way to share with this person to still achieve your purpose or goal of the conversation.
  - If you expect a negative response from someone, such as a denial of your experiences, consider involving another supporter in the conversation who can back you up in this conversation. You don't have to go it alone during these discussions!
  - Prepare yourself for someone to respond with an attempt at a consolation phrase; the person you're speaking with may respond in a way that may dismiss your experiences or try to find the "brighter side" of the situation, a potential response you're not looking for. Keep in mind they likely don't mean any harm, they may just be unsure of how to respond to what you've shared with them.

These invisible conversations are intended to help you open up to others around you to gain the understanding and support you need or want from others in personal, academic, and professional settings. During these conversations, you are not responsible for convincing others of your condition(s) or symptoms. There will likely always be people who will doubt or deny your experiences, but all that matters is your experiences and those who have your back no matter what your condition(s) throw your way.

Without speaking up or sharing our disabilities in some other way, there will be no way to understand just how many people are diagnosed with invisible disabilities or what they are experiencing because of their conditions. This type of isolation impacts people of any age, especially younger people who are still in school and making their way into early adulthood after high school or higher education. Oftentimes, others expect we are no different from them and do not consider what we may be going through in our lives, such as an invisible disability. This expectation of normalcy only strengthens when others expect young people to be healthy and able simply because of their age.

These invisible conversations can disrupt the silence around invisible disabilities of all kinds. The more conversations you have, the more support and understanding you may be able to gain from others to help you through highs and lows. Not only do these conversations make a personal impact, but also a societal impact, as these discussions will help to raise awareness about invisible disabilities and their effects on the people who have them.

These invisible conversations are not always easy to have. To get the discussion going, the first step is to often disclose your own experiences with your conditions or symptoms. This may be the end of the discussion, unless questions arise, or the topic comes up again at some point in the future. No matter the length or frequency of these conversations, they are often intensely personal one-sided exchanges. When I am the first to share my conditions with others, I am often the only one who can share some experiences about my invisible disability. This may be because I am the only one in the conversation with a condition, or because any others I'm speaking with don't feel comfortable adding their own stories.

Being the only one to open up about my conditions can be nerve-wrecking and isolating for me, regardless of whether this is the first conversation or the tenth one. When speaking about my conditions, I feel selfish when I speak about my experiences, and am careful not to sound like I'm complaining or like I'm a victim. I try to take up as little time as possible to provide information or answer any questions a person may ask me, despite my typical talkative nature. Deep down, a small voice within me tries to convince me the others I'm talking to will soon tire of hearing about my disabilities, and that I shouldn't burden them with these often-heavy conversations.

In her article *Burden vs. Entitlement,* author Carolanne Link shares her own struggles in finding a balance between being entitled to accommodations and extra support and being a burden on those around her.[49] She questions at what point she may be asking too much from others, ultimately compromising her independence. Feeling burdensome is a common concern for many people, even those without disabilities. Most people do not want to feel as though they are putting their family members, friends, colleagues, and so on in an

49   "Burden vs. Entitlement: A Disabled Person's Internal Battle," University of California, Los Angeles, Office of Information Technology Disabilities and Computing Program, accessed January 28, 2021.

awkward position by hampering them with their need for support and understanding.

Fortunately, a bigger part of me understands the value and necessity of these conversations and persuades me to keep sharing my stories. To help overcome my fears, I've found solace in the concept of positive curiosity, which can be shown in many forms and can come from many people and relationships. Positive curiosity is often first shown verbally or emotionally, such as when someone expresses interest or concern in my wellbeing. This can then develop into a willingness to support me in other ways. My friends at school will simply ask how I'm feeling when we're hanging out late at night at the end of our long week. My partner is perfectly content with staying in bed for the day when I'm feeling particularly fatigued.

Positive curiosity can come from people you'd never expect. In my freshman year of college, I gathered just enough courage to mention my chronic pain and mental conditions during an introduction presentation to other classmates. Tasked with sharing a handful of personal artifacts that described our personalities and identities, I chose to bring a sensory brush I had used to combat my sensitive skin as one of the seven items; as a part of my therapy, I would rub the brush over my skin to decrease pain and sensitivity over time. During the presentation, I heard the stories behind dozens of other items from my peers, which effectively replaced the nervousness I had felt when sharing my conditions.

Having mostly forgotten about my presentation, I was surprised when I was approached by two of my classmates the following week, and they mentioned my condition and the stories I shared in the previous class.

"Hey Alex, your condition is called Amplified Musculoskeletal Pain...Disease, right?" One of the two classmates tried to piece the name together, and I was stunned she even remembered my presentation, let alone most of the name of AMPS!

"Yeah, it's actually pain syndrome, but I'm surprised you remembered the rest of it." I felt a smile on my face as I experienced a sense of pleasant surprise and appreciation for her recollection.

"That's right, my bad. Nina and I were just looking at it and to read more about it, it sounds like it's pretty similar to fibromyalgia?" This short conversation continued, though the dialogue itself wasn't what impacted me; simply being invited to participate in this conversation about my disability made me feel as though I was cared for and I had some sort of effect on my classmates.

Finding others to share your experiences and struggles with can provide great practice for opening up within a supportive and understanding environment. These people motivate me to continue to share my experiences and begin these discussions about invisible disabilities. Not everyone you will meet will have this perspective, and it won't always be easy to identify the positively curious people around you, but I've managed to outline a handful of traits the positively curious people in my life have had in common. By searching for others with these characteristics, you'll be on your way to building a supportive community around you.

TRAITS OF POSITIVE CURIOSITY

ACTIVE LISTENING

From a young age, we're taught how to listen to others in a variety of settings, from one-on-one conversations to one presenter in front of a group. Active listening is a term I've become more familiar with recently, in which we focus entirely on the other person who is communicating with us, paying close attention to their words, tone, and body language to get a more accurate understanding of what the speaker is trying to say. Once we have fully grasped what this person has said, then we may respond with our interpretation and finally share our own perspectives.

I wouldn't necessarily tout myself as the best active listener, but I know what it feels like to speak with one. During these conversations, I feel as though I would be able to express my thoughts carefully and without interruption or fear of misunderstanding. As the exchange continues, I feel more comfortable with opening up about my highs and lows and vulnerabilities in every part of my life.

Besides the shared benefits of building trust and long-lasting connections, active listening can promote acceptance and understanding between people.[50] An active listening workbook from Futures Upfront highlights the benefit of a positive, non-judgmental mindset when entering conversations: "If you bring a mindset...of unconditional positive regard to your active listening, your listening will become

---

50   "Active Listening Skills: Definition and Examples," Indeed Career Guide, November 23, 2020.

much more open and accepting of whatever a person tells you."[51] This mindset provides an opportunity within invisible conversations to make a meaningful connection and sense of understanding between those in the conversation.

Good listeners have played an important role in understanding my own thoughts and feelings, even if they didn't necessarily have much to add to the conversation. At its simplest, a good listener can be a helpful resource to be able to open up to and even vent to during particularly difficult days. Beyond this, a good listener can also help you talk through your problems to find a solution. Listeners such as my mom, my partner, and a couple of friends have gotten me through periods of pain and uncertainty from my disabilities, and I'm grateful for their help. Just remember to trade the role of active listener so those listeners around you can have a turn.

PATIENCE

Patience is an admirable trait to have, especially in friendship or close relationships. It combines tolerance and understanding into one characteristic that can invite others to interact with one another without fear of interruption, judgment, or outburst during any interaction, including discussions. When I share my experiences with patient people, I feel as though I have the room to share my story at a pace and depth that is comfortable to me.

---

51   Maria Katrivesis and Barbel Winter, "Active Listening—Unconditional Positive Regard Across Cultures," (Sydney: futures Upfront, 2016), 4-10, futures Upfront.

When communicating with professors or teachers about my conditions and the accommodations I'll need, their patience is evident in their responses or conversations with me. To build tolerance within the people around me, I try to communicate with others early on. Before the start of a school year or semester, approximately a week prior to the start of class, I send emails that outline a brief description of my conditions and the accommodations I have applied to receive for the class.

Patience is particularly important in my circumstances, as I can never predict how I am going to feel days, weeks, or months into the semester. My pain and other symptoms can start and grow at a moment's notice which can impact my ability to keep up with assignments or other responsibilities. When I explain this predicament early on, I set myself up for patience and understanding from my professors at a later point in time, even when I won't be able to give much notice on the changes in my conditions. In cases that this understanding may be hard to come by, I've been able to fall back on the disability office at my school.

It's clear what it feels like to speak with an impatient person: you feel rushed when speaking to them, they may interrupt your conversation, or they may be quick to jump to conclusions during the conversation. Impatience is imminent, especially when emotions are running high or those around us are in a time crunch during group projects or impending deadlines, for example. But if someone is willing to maintain composure, even for a brief period, to gain a better understanding of my experiences and how they can support me, then they fulfill another trait of positive curiosity.

SYMPATHY

The last trait of positive curiosity, and what I believe to be the most important aspect, is sympathy. Both sympathy and empathy are applicable in this situation, but most of my interactions have been with others who do not experience an invisible disability, which may make them a sympathetic party. Sympathy refers to a sense of condolence for someone else's hardships, while empathy includes the ability to resonate with or relate to that challenge. Finally, a sense of compassion is the ability to commiserate with another person and take action to support them in some way.

Most of the positively curious people I've spoken with are sympathetic of my experiences with my pain or disabilities. They are unable to completely understand my struggles and triumphs specifically through the lens of a disability, but their ability to feel care and compassion for me naturally pushes them to ask questions, express concern, or share their sympathies when needed. Even if they don't have a physical, mental, or neurological condition, they are likely to be able to relate to at least a couple of my experiences through their own, encouraging mutual compassion and understanding for one another.

I believe there is a fine line between compassion and pity. People often have adverse reactions to pity, as they don't want to be looked down upon for what others may see as a misfortune. Dr. Aaron Ben-Zeév, a professor of philosophy, does a great job of explaining the difference between pity and compassion, which are two types of sympathy.[52]

---

52 "Do Not Pity Me," Psychology Today, August 14, 2010.

In his article, Dr. Ben-Zeév begins by providing an example for both pity and compassion: one may feel pity for the homeless and feel compassion for someone who is close to them who requires constant help, such as a loved one with a disability. The key difference between pity and compassion is the level of commitment and action taken to help another person.

Dr. Ben-Zeév writes, "Compassion involves the willingness to become personally involved, while pity usually does not. Pity is more spectator-like than compassion; we can pity people while maintaining a safe emotional distance from them. While pity involves the belief in the inferiority of the object, compassion assumes equality in a common humanity."

When people believe they may be able to make some sort of substantial impact on someone, then they are more willing to take action and become personally involved to help that person. Otherwise, as Dr. Ben-Zeév describes, pity is the scenario in which we can offer substantial or impactful help, but do not believe we can help or we are even obligated to help in the first place.

A compassionate response is much more likely when there is a long-term, ongoing relationship between people, in which at least one person will require some form of assistance or support for a longstanding period of time. As the saying goes, "Pity costs nothing, and it ain't worth nothing."[53] This feeling of regret or sadness for one's misfortune is unhelpful if it does

---

53 "'Pity Costs Nothing and Ain't Worth Nothing.' —Josh Billings," quotes, accessed January 28, 2021.

not involve some sort of action or commitment to make a difference in someone's life. Compassion can be viewed as pity in a more positive, proactive form that is beneficial for everyone. Sympathy, and the subsequent compassion that follows it, play an important role in positive curiosity within invisible conversations; these feelings are the catalysts behind one's desire to support someone they know with a disability.

On rare occasions, I find others who are positively curious and are empathetic with my experiences. Even if they do not have my specific conditions, they are able to find some commonalities between themselves and me, which inspires positive curiosity for one another. Most times, I am the first to share my disabilities, and occasionally another person with a disability is also willing to open up to me to share their own experiences.

Referring back to my story about my freshman year class presentation, I was working on another project with a classmate months after my speech about my conditions. We sat in the campus center one evening, working on an essay for our class. A natural silence in our workflow prompted her to change our conversation topic to mention my presentation from earlier in the semester.

"I never got to mention this, but I really enjoyed your presentation. I remember you mentioned your pain condition, what's it called again?" she asked as I pulled my attention away from our work.

"Oh, thanks! It's called Amplified Musculoskeletal Pain Syndrome, but it's also known as AMPS for short," I explained.

"Yeah, I haven't heard of that before. I actually have a chronic pain condition in my back that I've been dealing with for a long time, but I really don't like to share it with others," she explained.

She then continued to explain her fears of speaking out about her condition. Simply put, she didn't want others to look at her differently for having a disability or illness. Her condition affected her on a daily basis, but she made it a point to not mention it to others. While I was empathetic to her reasoning for not wanting to disclose her health to others, I felt relieved I wasn't alone as she was one of my first classmates who opened up to me about a disability.

We passed a few questions back and forth, gaining a better understanding of each other's conditions and treatments, and how we juggle school with everything we have to do. We were able to relate to one another and shared a patient conversation where we listened to each other and exchanged our experiences. Though the conversation was brief, I felt comforted by the idea there were others around me who knew what I was experiencing.

We've spoken a handful of times since this conversation, but the topic never came up again. I had attempted to encourage her to open up and speak to others, including professors and classmates, to get the support and understanding she may need during particularly tough times. She was adamant and insisted this information was easier to keep to herself. While I didn't have the same sharing philosophy, I could understand her hesitancy. It has been a long process figuring out how to share my experiences with others and understanding the supportive and positively curious people in my life. I often wish I didn't have to go through the same explanation with every professor and occasional classmate, but I know communication is key for my situation.

Positive curiosity is made up of a handful of incredibly simple traits or principles. We're often taught to listen, be patient, and have compassion for others as we grow. Because of this, it can be easy to gloss over the positively curious people in our lives, but we can often find them when we have invisible conversations about our disabilities. I invite you to think of the people around you who have displayed these traits when you've opened up about a disability or hardship. The people who ask questions, listen closely, and do what they can to help will be a strong source of support and understanding during your highs and lows. Practicing invisible conversations between yourself and those in your immediate support system will then prepare you for these conversations with others in your life.

CHAPTER 7

SHARING YOUR DISABILITY AT SCHOOL

———

I began to lose control of my body at a very young age. I was unable to move the way I wanted to, do different activities, or function like a "normal" person without my pain interrupting me. Over the years, I shied away from doing the things that hurt me; this meant no more morning walks around the town with my mom, or running, jumping, tumbling with friends in our front yards. I couldn't commit to any sports teams as I grew older and could only stand to play tennis with my mom until my body begged me to stop.

Since I couldn't control my body, I assumed I could instead control my mind and intellect. As a student, that translated to exerting my control over my schoolwork and grades. Ever since I began school, teachers would describe me as a smart and respectful student. Many wished everyone else in the class could be like me. The parent-teacher conference meetings were my favorite time of year as I relished in these praises. From this point, I made it my mission to reach the top of each class. The recognition I received over the years filled the hole left behind from my pain and physical disabilities.

This recognition molded into a reputation as I began to be labeled as a teacher's pet and goody-two shoes. Typically, classmates only wished to work with me on homework and projects so they could ensure they would receive the high grade I would work to earn for the both of us. At its best, I was ranked among top performing students and enjoyed awards such as honor roll, National Honor Society, and academic scholarships. At its worst, others accused me of cheating or bribing teachers to give me an A+.

My grades didn't come without work. I spent countless amounts of time, energy, and tears pouring over my homework, projects, and exams. Anxiety and stress plagued me every time I even thought about school, despite my school track record and natural inclination toward academics. My mental and physical struggles felt disconnected and unrelated; the underlying connection became apparent when I was finally diagnosed with Amplified Musculoskeletal Pain Syndrome, or AMPS.

I would come to find out my bodily pain was triggered and worsened by stress, creating an endless cycle of tension, pain, and frustration caused by my symptoms. I felt ridiculous for not being able to see my connection to my stress and my pain sooner. It took a while for me to recognize the irony of my situation: I sought to control my grades to make up for the lack of control over my pain, and the stress that resulted from my schooling and other worries ended up making my pain even worse. Even after I made this connection, I struggled to understand how I would be able to just simply stop stressing so much over my grades. My confidence and self-esteem had been built upon my high marks, and if I were to remove that foundation, then where would that leave me? Who would I be without my grades?

I was unwilling to redefine myself immediately after this diagnosis, and I was also still hesitant about sharing my pain with everyone around me, so I continued through the rest of high school without disclosing my disability to others. Communication between teachers only occurred when I was recovering from my concussions and required extra time or assistance on assignments. A couple of closer friends knew I had some health issues but didn't know how much it impacted me every day. Everyone else around me was none the wiser to my diagnosis and ongoing treatment journey.

Since no one knew this new development, I maintained my high grades and therefore continued to stress over my education. My AMPS specialists insisted I must learn how to manage my stress and anxiety to manage my pain. But as the classes became more difficult, my anxiety managed to increase even more, as I was now concerned over the possibility of not pulling off A's in my classes. I struggled to choose between prioritizing my health, the only thing that allowed me to function, or my grades, which were what I believed to be the foundation of who I was.

As I've moved on from middle school to high school to college, my symptoms have changed and progressed, mostly for the worse. As a result, I've also changed who I share my experiences with over time. Prior to my AMPS diagnosis, I didn't share my difficulties with anyone at school. I think the school nurse was the only one who knew I was having some pain, but my complaints never left the nurse's office.

In the months leading up to my diagnosis, I had tried to share my symptoms with others, almost like an experiment. I wanted to find out how others would respond to me, specifically within a school context. I practiced sharing my symptoms and diagnoses with administrators, teachers, and peers as I aimed to find a way to open up about my conditions to get the help I needed.

There was a different dynamic for each group, as I first divulged my conditions to school administrators, then teachers, and eventually classmates. Over the years, I've learned how to craft my story depending on who I am sharing with and why I am sharing with them within an academic context.

FACULTY & ADMINISTRATORS

When I first began experiencing chronic pain from AMPS, my teachers were some of the very few people in my life who knew what was going on. I found it difficult to keep these problems to myself, especially during elementary school, as I would make daily trips to the nurse's office for my sore back and stomach aches. Because of this, my teachers either believed I was making up my pain to get out of class or they thought something was genuinely wrong.

I didn't have an explanation or diagnosis until high school, so I struggled to explain to my teachers what was going on with me. It's easy to excuse a doctor's appointment here or there, but when I was out of class at least once a week every week for a doctor's appointment or diagnostic test, I felt as though I fell to the wayside in the classroom and school as a whole.

Before high school, I avoided sharing my pain with teachers or other school administrators as much as possible, even if I felt as though I could describe what I was feeling, I was fearful they would doubt me, just like my doctors had. I assumed I was better off keeping my pain to myself, even as the disconnect continued to grow between me and my school life.

I finally received a diagnosis early on in high school, just as my pain worsened. By this point, I struggled to get out of bed every morning and make it to school. My body would hurt so much I hobbled around the hallways and constantly shifted in my chair, attempting to alleviate my pain. Once I was diagnosed with AMPS, I felt as though my experiences were justified enough to share with my guidance counselor and my teachers.

I worked with my AMPS specialists to craft a letter that explained what AMPS was, what symptoms I was experiencing, and what could be done to help me at school. I went to my guidance counselor with this note, assuming she could serve as the messenger to my teachers every year by distributing the note and approving my accommodations.

However, this didn't go according to my plan, as my guidance counselor was one of my biggest opponents throughout high school. She never seemed to believe my pain and symptoms, even when she had a doctor's note in her hand. She would eventually distribute the note to my teachers but failed to be a source of support in scenarios in which a teacher may deny an accommodation. Since fighting against my guidance counselor discouraged me, I decided to go right to my teachers at the start of every schoolyear. With my doctor's note attached, I copied and pasted an email to every teacher explaining my condition and the impact it has on me. I invited teachers to reach out to me with any questions or concerns and promised to maintain communication throughout the schoolyear or semester. When I started, I avoided directly asking for accommodations. I felt as though I didn't have anyone backing me to be able to ask for personal adjustments, as if a doctor's note wasn't enough to explain what I needed and why.

To combat this, I collaborated with my doctors to understand what accommodations would be reasonable for my conditions. I would express what I believed would be helpful to me, and my physicians would find a balance between accommodating my needs and not excusing me from too many activities. Finally, I would request this information be put into the note that would also explain my conditions and their symptoms. By doing this, the doctor's note did most of the work on my behalf when I distributed it to my teachers, and I felt more validation for my adjustments. In most situations, teachers were more than willing to do what they could to help after being offered consistent communication and actionable accommodations that they could agree with in the classroom.

However, there would be the occasional teacher who wouldn't grant my accommodations or seemed ignorant of my disabilities. A few teachers didn't believe I was in pain. A couple others believed their class was too important for me to leave a few minutes early each day or miss a homework assignment on a particularly painful day, so the recommended accommodations were denied. Few could understand how my stress worsened my pain, which I struggled to explain in the first place. Since I had put so much care into my grades and schoolwork, I would stress about school every day. I couldn't quite figure out how to tell teachers or professors, "Hey, your class is giving me debilitating back pain." I also couldn't determine if it was up to me to stop stressing so much or if I should look to my teachers to cut me some slack.

I did what I could to explain the causes of my pain through the doctor's note and my own means of communication. But this lack of awareness or misunderstanding about my conditions could make it difficult to get the support I needed, and it wasn't necessarily to the fault of myself or my teachers. While I've been able to find more compassionate professors upon entering college, this blameless unawareness continues to be a problem.

Kaitlyn, an acquaintance of mine, is a pre-med student who grapples with Crohn's disease. She explained how her Crohn's prevented her from earning the grades she worked toward. On many occasions, her exams were interrupted by health emergencies, but she wasn't granted additional preparation or review her peers had received. While her professors and advisors were aware of her condition, they didn't seem to understand what should've been done to accommodate her during these times of need.

"When I had spoken with advisors about these [health] concerns, specifically in regard to my medical school admissions, many have asked me, 'do you think this will be a temporary thing?'" she shared. "Crohn's disease is a chronic illness, meaning I will face challenges for the rest of my life. Hearing people say I might not be good enough because of my illness can be very disheartening."

More often than not, our teachers, professors, and advisors are unaware of the weight of their words. This lack of awareness is one of the many factors that makes having an invisible illness while in school difficult and particularly frustrating. In my experience, I've found the first step to raising awareness and building understanding is through communication.

I can decide for myself what I want to share with my instructors about my conditions and what accommodations I will need. My conditions are always in flux, and by offering on-going communication about any changes and support I may need, I've found my teachers and professors are often more than willing to help as they are positively curious about my conditions and my experiences with them. This support can come in the form of extra help on some topics, more time to complete an assignment, or an offer to lay low during class. There could be more accommodation options open to you depending on your condition(s) and your symptoms, and how they impact your schoolwork.

Consider some of the following accommodation categories and how they may be applicable to suit your accommodation needs at school:

- **Presentation**—modifying how information is presented or shared through lessons and homework, such as larger print textbooks, audiobooks, or instructions provided orally.

- **Student response**—accommodating how you can respond to assignments, such as using audio recorders to orally record assignment responses or essays or taking oral exams.
- **Setting**—modifying the environment around you, such as distraction-free testing or preferential seating in the classroom.[54] [55]
- **Scheduling & timing**—modifying when assignments are administered to you, as well as the amount of time allowed for you to complete it. This can include taking exams at different times than peers, being allowed breaks during assignments, and extended time for timed assignments or tests.[56] [57] [58]

These are just some categories and examples of accommodations that may help you in the classroom. It's important to work together with your healthcare team, school administrators, and teachers to make sure your needs are met. However, should you find obstacles like I did, don't be afraid to speak up and advocate for yourself.

To do this, I advise you and your guardians understand your rights in school in the United States. For this, personal

---

54   "Accommodations for Students with LD," LD Online, accessed February 5, 2021.

55   "Common Accommodations and Modifications in School," Understood for All Inc., accessed February 5, 2021.

56   "Supports, Modifications, and Accommodations for Students," Center for Parent Information & Resources, February 8, 2020.

57   LD Online, "Accommodations for Students."

58   Morin, "Common Accommodations."

research into your rights based on your condition will be most helpful, but here are a handful of disability rights, laws, or acts to start your search:

TITLE II OF THE AMERICANS WITH DISABILITIES ACT (ADA)

- The ADA provides civil rights protections to people with disabilities in many aspects of their lives, including public schools. This law prohibits discrimination against people with disabilities.[59]
- The ADA defines a disability as the following: "A physical or mental impairment that substantially limits one or more major life activities, a person who has a history or record of such an impairment, or a person who is perceived by others as having such an impairment."[60]

SECTION 504 OF THE REHABILITATION ACT

- Section 504 is another antidiscrimination law that provides civil rights protections to people with disabilities in programs or settings that receive federal funding, which includes most public schools.[61]
- Section 504 defines an individual with a disability as a "person with a physical or mental impairment which substantially limits one or more major life activities. People who have a history of, or who are regarded as having a physical or mental impairment that substantially limits

---

59 "Your Rights Under Section 504 of the Rehabilitation Act," Office for Civil Rights, US Department of Health and Human Services, revised June, 2006.

60 "Information and Technical Assistance on the Americans with Disabilities Act," ADA.gov, accessed February 5, 2021.

61 Office for Civil Rights, "Your Rights."

one or more major life activities, are also covered [under Section 504]."[62]

THE INDIVIDUALS WITH DISABILITIES EDUCATION ACT (IDEA)

- IDEA is a statute that ensures access to appropriate free public education to eligible students, including special education and related services, covering students from birth until the age of twenty-one or time of twelfth grade graduation.[63]
- IDEA defines covered individuals as "A child with specific disabilities who, by reason thereof, needs specially designed instruction and related services."[64]

Since coming to college, I've found a more accepting environment for my conditions. Through rights granted to me by the Americans with Disabilities Act and my college's learning center for students with disabilities, many obstacles have been removed from my path to obtaining my accommodations, thankfully without even needing to mention my entitlement to my rights as an individual with a disability. But for those who may find more roadblocks in their way, additional personal research will be vital to understanding your coverage and your resources if you find yourself being denied reasonable accommodations.

Each year, I learn a better way to communicate my illnesses and symptoms clearly so others can understand how these

---

62 "Your Rights Under Section 504 of the Rehabilitation Act," Office for Civil Rights, US Department of Health and Human Services, revised June, 2006.

63 "About IDEA," Individuals with Disabilities Education Act, US Department of Education, accessed February 5, 2021.

64 Southwest ADA Center, "Disability Rights."

conditions can impact me in school. Though I can never anticipate my professors' response, consistent communication through invisible conversations has served as the best tool for me to get the understanding and support I need from my teachers, professors, and advisors.

CLASSMATES & PEERS

My peers were unaware of the issues I faced with my health. Throughout all of elementary and middle school, I had no idea how to explain my symptoms to others. Even when I received a diagnosis in high school, I avoided telling classmates about my health complications out of fear of additional bullying and ridicule. I didn't trust my classmates to take my symptoms and conditions seriously, so I never bothered to open up to them.

Often times, I attempted to cover my health emergencies up by providing vague or sarcastic responses. However, avoiding the topic or attempting to throw people off through my replies never really worked out, as the mockery from others would seep through the excuses I tried to give them.

During my sophomore year when I woke up one morning to get ready for school, I remember swinging my legs over the side of the couch I had slept on and began to stand before both of my ankles gave out on me. The pain forced me back onto the couch and I cried out, frustrated that my ankles were hurting again. This same episode had happened months prior during my freshman year, so I already became used to using crutches to support myself.

After calling out to my mom, my crutches were retrieved from the basement and I continued to get ready for the school day ahead. By my third class of the day, I had grown used to the stares and questions from classmates. I didn't have an extravagant or daring story to explain my sudden injury, so I resorted to my one sentence explanation: "I just woke up, got out of bed, and couldn't stand or walk." My classmates knew as much about my injury as I did.

I hobbled to another class in the latter half of the day and took my seat, attempting to ignore the feel of stares as I made my way into the classroom. Once I was seated, I felt a tap on my shoulder as my classmate inevitably asked what happened to me. I offered the same reply I gave to others who had asked throughout the day while I steadied my crutches against my desk. I turned toward him again and watched a smug smirk spread across his face before he began his reply.

"The teacher must have screwed you so hard you couldn't walk—no wonder why you have an A."

To this day, I replay this exchange over and over again in my head; I still haven't thought of a reply, even in my wildest imagination. I can't remember what I said in that moment if I replied at all. I sincerely hope I said something, *anything*, in reply.

Ever since I began school, I understood kids could be vicious and cruel for any reason at all, even by accident. As I got older, the comments became more intentional, as we were all old enough to understand the meaning and weight of our words. If I were to visibly put weight on one leg over the other, I would be called a "cripple." For the many years I couldn't participate in gym class or sports, I was called lazy. Sometimes disclosing my pain to others added fuel to the fiery barrage of comments and ridicule.

Bullying was a common theme I found from speaking to others with invisible disabilities. Classmates can find anything to mock about anyone but having a condition that makes us particularly different makes us an easy target for harassment.

One parent shared the story of her daughter's life with Amplified Musculoskeletal Pain Syndrome. A natural athlete from a young age, she was forced to stop playing team sports when her pain became too much for her to bear. Her mother shared that playing on a local sports team was highly regarded by residents of their town, and the bonds formed through these teams were "impenetrable."

Since her daughter dropped out of her basketball and field hockey teams, she lost most of her connections to other teammates, thus being alienated and isolated by the groups she used to be part of.

Another AMPS patient named Addison faced similar problems as she was forced to drop out of her softball team. But as her pain progressed even further, her school forced her into homebound learning since she missed so much school due to doctors' appointments or pain flare days. Addison's classmates were vocal about their confusion and conclusions about her condition; Addison shares how every day her peers would ask what's wrong with her.

Addison's mom shares, "When kids would find out she was at another doctor's appointment or emergency room visit, they would tell her she's faking it and just wanted attention." It still baffles me how people can accuse a child, who is forced out of their school, sports, hobbies, and so on, of just looking for attention. This inability to participate and interact with peers can leave children feeling isolated, but insult is added to injury when a child's symptoms are dismissed as means for gaining attention.

Intentionally harmful words and actions can stick with you for a long time and do some major damage to your self-esteem. But the seemingly innocuous comments tended to hurt me more: "I wish I could sit out every gym class." "At least you don't look like there's something wrong with you."

On particularly difficult days, even a lasting stare from classmates would shake me to my core. It felt as though they were trying to watch me long enough to show my pain or my symptoms were real. I became paranoid that people were always staring at me, despite there being no visual difference between myself and someone without a visible disability.

Similarly, Addison shared another story with me about school. She explains it was becoming more obvious to classmates and teachers that she was sick. In one instance, she collapsed in the middle of the hallway one morning, surrounded by classmates and peers. She described this experience as one of the most embarrassing moments in her illness. "I can still feel the burning stares."

Over the years of speaking with classmates throughout early education, high school, and college, I've come to learn that some of my peers simply weren't mature enough to understand and accept my condition. Unfortunately, that maturity may never come, so I had to separate myself from people who looked down on me for my disabilities.

This was my tactic for all of middle and high school. I was able to find and stick by a couple of friends who understood what I was going through and did my best to ignore the rest. My experience in K–12 school was what pushed me to go to school out-of-state, far away from those who thought they knew me.

I did what I could to express my experiences to my peers—describing my symptoms, sharing what it's like to have a condition and go to all these appointments, and explaining how my condition can impact me at school. However, I think it's important to mention I made the decision to share my story with others to try to gain understanding. As someone with a disability, I don't think it's my job to make others understand. I learned there's only so much I can do to try to make others see what is going on below the surface, but if they can't understand that then it's not my responsibility to keep pushing them. I believe communication is the best way to gain support and understanding from others. However, support and understanding are different from respect, which is something many classmates didn't show me. You should never feel as though you need to explain yourself to get the respect you deserve from others.

Because of this belief, I stopped working so hard to work with my peers and classmates to understand my condition.

For most, there was nothing I could do to show them their words and actions were wrong. At a certain point, I made the personal decision to just keep pushing through to the end of each school year.

Fortunately, this dynamic changed when I came to college. As I settled into my new environment, I eventually felt comfortable around my new classmates. I felt emboldened by being in a new place where no one knew me, and I was determined to make the most out of my college experience with my disabilities.

I shared my experiences a little at a time as I became more comfortable around others, this comfort at least partly due to increased maturity from my peers. First, I would only share my pain or mention my conditions if someone asked. Eventually, I became adjusted to telling classmates about my symptoms if they would impede on our groupwork. Finally, I learned how to share my disabilities with others in any context, whenever I want to share them. I worked my way up over time, becoming more vocal as I tried telling new people in different contexts to observe their responses. I expanded from sharing with close friends to disclosing my conditions to classmates and project partners. The more comfortable I was, the more vocal I could be about my experience with my disabilities.

It's important to remember sharing your disabilities is a personal decision, especially when it comes to classmates and peers who may not understand what you're going through. You can decide how, when, and with who you can disclose your conditions to, if you choose to do so at all. You will find a number of people along the way who may not believe your circumstances, and even worse, may exclude or mock you for them. However, the key is to keep forging ahead to find your positively curious supporters and to lean on them as you progress through life.

CHAPTER 8

TALKING WITH FRIENDS & PARTNERS

———

FRIENDS

Growing up, I struggled to make many friends, but the struggle wasn't obvious to me until years later. Even prior to the start of my pain, I didn't have many friends around me in school and at home. When I began to develop symptoms, starting with back pain and constant headaches, the small number of friendships fell even more.

When my pain began in elementary school, it wasn't immediately clear to me that others my age didn't feel this way. I didn't know experiencing deep back pain or excruciating stomach aches every day was abnormal. So when I began to complain about my symptoms and started going to doctors' appointments, those around me, including friends, soon noticed I was different from them.

That perceived difference resulted in many ended friendships over the years. Throughout elementary and early middle school, I had several friends who came and went. Over time, my ability to participate in certain activities was taken away. Those who I *thought* were my friends began to cut ties as I could no longer run and tumble outside, play sports, or jump on the trampoline. If we couldn't play like they wanted to, then I wasn't the kind of friend they wanted.

As I struggled to keep up with the few friendships I had, closer connections were being created between others, thus leaving me behind; it always seemed the current friend I was closest to ended up being closer with someone else instead. This resulted in me being that "last choice" friend: the person others would hang out with only if all of their other friends were unavailable.

At the height of my pain during middle school and high school, it was difficult to conceal my symptoms from those around me, especially in school. At this time, I also learned who was really on my side and cared for me as a friend. As I was bullied and mocked by my peers with the people I called "friends" on the sidelines, it was clear to me how little they cared for me and our friendship.

When I was at my lowest in terms of my health and self-esteem, I fooled myself into thinking I had genuine friends, when in actuality they didn't treat me like a true friend. During this time, I took verbal and physical abuse from people I thought were my friends. A handful of them would be rough with me almost every day at school, hitting me, kicking me, asking "does this hurt? What about this?" I convinced myself this is what friends do and almost never spoke up for myself, even when I didn't feel that this was right. I suppose I thought I was better off not saying anything so I wouldn't lose the couple of people who would talk to and be civil with me for at least much of our time spent together.

Out of the five or six relationships I would consider friendships in early high school, only one or two were true friends. The remaining group dropped off one by one as we moved from grade to grade and class to class. Other friendships came and went over the years, none particularly memorable to me now. By the end of high school, I graduated with the same two true friends I had from the start.

Over the years, and even to this day, we go through phases of on-and-off talking and hanging out. Since I decided to go to a college states away, the distance would keep us apart for periods of time. But no matter how long it had been, we've always come back to one another. These two friends have taught me what friendship is supposed to be like. We all have our own challenges in our lives, but mutual support is all around despite the differences. We are not all always able to relate to each other's problems. I'd consider myself to be the friend that has the greatest health challenges, but my friends are still sympathetic and understanding about my problems, just as I am with theirs.

My lesson on having friendships while having invisible disabilities was a difficult one to learn but I'm glad I learned it before coming to college. When I visited my campus for the first time, I could tell this would be a completely different atmosphere from my hometown, and I looked forward to forging new friendships there.

Along with more maturity came more understanding for my conditions, as all my friends have shown their support for me during all my highs and lows. College was a bit of a transition, which did impact my health, but I've been fortunate to have the right friends with me to help me through the four years. I've spoken with several others my age who have also gained great support from their friends throughout their health journeys. It seems we all had a difficult time making friends at different points in our lives because of our disabilities.

Kaitlyn, a current college student with Crohn's disease, reflected on the impact her condition has on her friendships, and vice versa: "I have been very fortunate in that most of my friends are supportive and understanding. I have had a few people in the past accuse me of using my Crohn's symptoms as an excuse to avoid social gatherings because of how frequent my pain occurred. I have trouble maintaining relationships with these types of people because they do not understand or even attempt to understand my struggle."

This misunderstanding can likely stem from immaturity or a lack of sympathy from those around us. It can feel as though you are pressured to "be a good friend," which to some, can include always hanging out and doing activities you might not be comfortable with. It can be exhausting trying to maintain these friendships and can negatively impact your health if you continue to pursue friendships with others who don't consider your perspective and experiences. Fortunately, Kaitlyn does have a number of friends who have been understanding or supportive of her experiences that she can lean on, even when others don't believe her.

Addison, a current high school student with AMPS, also recounted some more personal examples of her struggle with friendships. Addison mentioned the hardships she faced during her first few years at a new school as her symptoms had begun to worsen. She told me during her first year at the new school she had no friends, and her twice-a-week doctors' appointments that kept her out of school posed a threat to her ability to make new friends.

When Addison returned to school the next year after being put on homebound by the administrators, the problems persisted. Addison was kept home from school for several months, her only interactions with her school coming from the teachers who visited her for one-on-one tutoring. This gap in school involvement made Addison an easy target when she finally went back to class with her peers: "I had girls telling me I couldn't sit with them like they owned the table. They'd call me names, and the people I thought were my friends just sat there. I started eating lunch alone or in a classroom."

During these difficulties with making friends, Addison turned to her family members for support. When I asked what resources she wished she had during this time, she told me she wishes she knew she wasn't alone, and that there were others her age who were faced with similar adversities. Addison's mom, Lori, mentioned Addison hopes to start a podcast for kids with chronic conditions to show them they are not alone, like she thought she was.

By reflecting on my own experiences, and hearing about the experiences of others, I've come to understand no relationship is worth any amount of ridicule or abuse, no matter how small it may seem. Having a close friend can make all the difference when you are faced with a tough time, including declines in health. At a younger age, there will be many peers who will not understand what it's like to have a disability or illness, and that can be incredibly isolating. There will be others who will continue to assume that since you are young, you should be healthy and able to do the things everyone else can supposedly do.

My advice is to continue to search for a quality friend that is positively curious, and can either empathize or sympathize with your situation, just as you can do for theirs. When I went away to college, I was nervous about leaving behind my only two friends from public school, but their kindness and support also encouraged me to keep reaching out to make more friends in this new environment. The friends you find may not be able to completely understand your experiences, but it can be enough to have someone who is there for you in spite of that.

PARTNERS & SIGNIFICANT OTHERS

As I grew older and my conditions progressed, I began to worry how my disabilities would impact different aspects of my personal life. Judging by the difficulty I experienced with friendships due to my symptoms, I expected similar problems in other areas, including dating.

I was never really self-conscious about my disabilities, but it took a while to understand how different I was from others my age because of my health struggles. When dating became a possibility in late middle school, it seemed as though I couldn't find anyone who was mature enough to understand and support me along my health journey. As expected, we were all young and childish; it took me a while to realize no one would understand my perspective at such a young age without experiencing it themselves.

I think this is one of the things that makes my relationship with my boyfriend Brandon so extraordinary. When we began dating at the start of my freshman year of high school, he provided me with immediate and unwavering support, even if he didn't completely understand my symptoms and conditions.

For a long time, I never really wanted to ask him about what he thought about my disabilities. I was worried about stirring the pot by asking questions, so I simply accepted his support without question. I felt we were better off not really talking about the impact my conditions may or may not have on our relationship.

This avoidance ended once I began writing this book. As always, Brandon has been incredibly supportive of me, and this book writing process is no exception. But when he began to ask about getting involved by reading my chapters and doing interviews, I felt this was the time to break the silence around the topic of my disabilities and our relationship.

Through our interview, I would divulge my fears for the future. I expressed my fear for the uncertainty that lay ahead in my life because of my conditions, and how these potential changes would impact our future, assuming there was one.

I shared the small sense of guilt I had begun to build as I considered how I may drag him and us down with me if my disabilities were to progress.

I asked a range of questions, seeking his perspective on the past, present, and future of our relationship and my conditions. Through this conversation, Brandon was quick to assuage every fear I harbored from the start of our relationship. From his perspective, my conditions didn't make any impact on our relationship. He had little-to-no concern about the future, as he expressed his care and understanding for my symptoms even during the uncertainty ahead.

He reflected on how my conditions have shaped me in his eyes: "I think you're a lot stronger and can get through things easier [because of your conditions]. You've proved to yourself you can do so much, despite the disabilities. Because of how you've reacted to these [health challenges], your disabilities have improved your character traits. That's not to say I'd want you to have your disabilities, but it has shaped who you are and has carved you more than others who didn't have these conditions."

It took several years to ask the questions I've been weighing in my mind, but the feelings of doubt faded with each question he answered and emboldened my sense of confidence in myself and our relationship, despite my earlier wariness. If you find yourself in a similar situation to mine, I encourage you to not hide behind your fear or doubt about what your partner may say. If you're involved in a long-term relationship that your condition may have an impact on, you'll be better off asking these questions sooner than I did.

A couple of people I've interviewed about their invisible disabilities shared details about their relationships and the dynamic between their relationship and their conditions. These interviewees that referenced their partners highlighted the unwavering support they have received from their significant other, each one a little bit different from the rest.

For some interviewees, their partners were in the picture before the start of the diagnosis and treatment process. This was the case for Derek, who has multiple sclerosis. He described how he received his MS diagnosis on the same day as his one-year anniversary with his girlfriend and how this has impacted their relationship. "She's been my rock and so incredibly supportive. I remember us joking about how she's stuck with me now because 'what kind of jerk leaves someone with Multiple Sclerosis?'"

Others began experiencing symptoms and underwent treatments during their relationships, such as Stephanie who has Lupus and Phil who has Type 1 Diabetes. They both shared the dynamics of their relationships and how they are altered by their conditions.

In Stephanie's case, she's been with her husband for nine years now. She explained how he has shown his support, such as taking her to appointments and sticking by her side when her symptoms are at their worst. She reflected on the importance of finding a partner who will do their best to understand and support your experiences. "You have to find a partner who understands there are days where you're not going to be able to do things."

"I got lucky—my husband understands I have days where I'm just not getting off the couch, and he's left with the cooking and cleaning," she continued. "But then you have the days where you feel good, and you have to try to not guilt yourself into overworking yourself to make up for the days you were on the couch."

She capped off her reflection with a piece of advice for others with disabilities in relationships: "Find somebody who is a partner, and not just a spouse, and somebody who understands not every day is going to be split fifty-fifty."

Phil shared his appreciation for his wife who has helped him with his modified diet and other treatments for his Type 1 Diabetes: "My wife has always been a huge supporter and always has my back. So, she was ready to help the day I was diagnosed. She helps me count carbs when making meals and she made sure I was checking up on my blood sugar. I couldn't ask for a better support role in my life."

By hearing stories from others, I've learned the many shapes and forms of support significant others can provide to their partner who is dealing with a disability. Even though each relationship dynamic is unique, I found it comforting to hear from others about their experiences maintaining a partnership while managing a disability. I don't believe there is one right way to show up for your partner to let them know you're there for them, regardless of whether or not they have a chronic condition.

In the age of social media, there is no shortage of personal blogs and accounts from young people with disabilities, as well as their significant others. While embracing the uniqueness of your partnership, keep in mind you have resources out there and that it's okay to look for ideas from others on how they manage their disabilities and their romantic relationships.

One of the most helpful blogs I've found comes from writer Sam Dylan Finch on *Everyday Feminism*. Finch describes his relationship with his partner, who struggles with fibromyalgia, chronic fatigue, anxiety, and depression, among other diagnoses. Finch shares his perspective and lessons learned as the partner of someone with an invisible disability.[65] You can pick the advice that is most applicable to you and your situation, but I think these three lessons are important for all partners to hear, the first being your partner should love you for who you are right now. Finch writes, "It's difficult to accept our loved ones in the moment, without getting swept up into who they were prior to their disability (if the onset was later) or who we would like them to be in the future."[66] More often than not, we are not in control of our disabilities. Because of this, it's important to find a partner who recognizes the future of your condition is unknown, and expecting better days ahead can be damaging to both of you.

Second, your partner should understand there will be times in which they cannot help you. You are not a problem to be fixed, and both you and your partner should recognize that. There will be challenges that don't have ideal solutions but seeking comfort in the presence of their support can be just enough to combat each obstacle. Finch shares his lesson in

---

65 Sam Dylan Finch, "5 Lessons I've Learned as the Partner of Someone with an Invisible Disability," *Everyday Feminism*, July 2, 2015.

66 Ibid.

which he understands, "my partner just wanted me to help make the everyday a little better."[67]

Finally, and perhaps most importantly, is remembering how crucial it is for both you and your partner to practice self-care. Just as you do, a partner who truly cares for you can become worn down by the stress surrounding a chronic condition. Stress is unavoidable in any relationship, but when disability causes additional tension, self-care is that much more important. Finch expresses his struggle between support, self-care, and guilt, sharing, "It can feel selfish to have a good day when your partner is in bed, trying to manage their pain. You might even feel a little guilty about it, too. But it doesn't do anyone any good if you're sinking into the quicksand of despair—it's not good for you OR your loved one."[68]

You'll be able to decide what advice and resources are applicable to your relationship, but I think these three points are the start of a strong foundation to build your relationship from. In my own experience, I do what I can to communicate my experiences to Brandon since we are not able to be in each other's company most of the time. I'm honest about my symptoms and what's going on with me; I also try to share if there's anything I think he can do to help so he doesn't feel a sense of helplessness as I battle my pain and other symptoms. You may be avoiding a difficult conversation with your partner pertaining to your disability, but the sooner this conversation takes place, the better. These conversations can prepare you and your partner for whatever future that may come.

---

67 Ibid.
68 Ibid.

CHAPTER 9

SHARING YOUR DISABILITY AT WORK

———

Since I am just beginning my professional life, I haven't really experienced much of what it is like to grapple with my disabilities in the workplace. I had a few jobs throughout high school but struggled to stick around for more than a couple months due to difficulties with my anxiety, so I never considered it worthwhile to mention my predicament.

However, my two most recent jobs gave me pause to begin to consider the implications of having invisible disabilities while working in demanding roles. Despite this recent consideration, work continued to be one of the few places I didn't commonly share my disabilities as I was trying to build my reputation as a reliable coworker and leader. I never had any reason to believe my coworkers would treat me differently or resent me because of my conditions, but it wasn't a risk I was ready to take within my first year of starting my newest role.

During my sophomore year of college, I began my part-time job at my campus' new makerspace. Within three months of starting the role, I was promoted to one of three student-employee managers. Having been promoted so quickly, I felt pressure to show my fellow managers and coworkers I was more than capable of meeting the expectations of the role. At the time, I believed my disabilities to be a weakness, and I felt disclosing my conditions would put me in a vulnerable light and convince others I was not capable of taking on difficult tasks.

I did my best to hide my symptoms and their impact on me while I was on-shift, but I couldn't fake my health for long, especially as my hours increased from my recent promotion. I began to amble around the building, seeking relief for my back pain from sitting for more than one hour. I asked for extra help lifting items other able bodies may have been able to grab on their own. I implored my coworkers to climb up ladders on my behalf, as my fear of heights from my concussions would leave me hysterical.

I developed a sense of guilt for relying on my coworkers so heavily, when I hoped they would look to me for a can-do attitude and capability. As one of the student-managers, I took pride in my initiative as a leader. While I stepped up to the plate for many other tasks and projects, I felt embarrassed that I insisted my coworkers do some tasks instead. In these moments, it seemed as though the rest of my work had been invalidated because I couldn't complete some simple assignments, like climbing a ladder to retrieve a poster.

Not only did I take pride in my initiative as a manager, but also as a woman. In a space with various tools and machinery,

I started my first day by getting my hands dirty, attempting to prove I could do anything my male coworkers could do. I did my best to learn every piece of equipment and would volunteer for physically taxing assignments to prove my ability. These were points in which I traded my physical and mental well-being in exchange for the guise of capability and confidence.

I heard of a similar situation from Kaitlyn when I asked about the impact her Crohn's disease has on her and her job on her university's campus. She deals with several symptoms, ranging from frequent bathroom trips to stomach aches to extreme fatigue. Despite it all, in addition to classes, she works as a bike EMT and is part of a research lab at her school. By taking on these roles while tending to her condition, she's had to make a handful of changes in her daily life to juggle all obligations. She's requested a reduced course load to better manage her condition and receives testing accommodations to allow bathroom breaks as needed. Her weekly schedule is built around her job shifts, ensuring she gets enough sleep and can take her medications on time. She's involved in a lot of activities despite the time her condition takes away from her.

Kaitlyn mentions the feeling of inadequacy because of her condition despite her successes with the accommodations she's built for herself. Her role as a bike EMT for the university community is a particularly physically demanding job, and shifts can last as long as eleven hours. At a baseline, she requires recurrent breaks and battles frequent pains. On her most difficult days, she is unable to get out of bed, struggling to see to her daily obligations. Kaitlyn mentioned her coworkers have been very understanding, but she still feels a sense of inadequacy. "Since many members of the group plan to go into the medical field, they understand the need to prioritize my health. However, I often feel like a burden or a subpar member."

Intrigued by the similarities between my experiences and Kaitlyn's, I wanted to learn more about what it's like to enter the workforce and have a full-time job with a disability. At the time, I pursued this research to inform myself in time for my graduation in May in hopes I had secured a full-time position. I was relieved to find similar stories and potential resources for people with invisible and visible disabilities in the workplace prior to my entering the workforce.

I discovered dozens of stories from young people with disabilities and how they juggled their conditions, the recruitment process, and their jobs. I felt uplifted by their experiences as my fear of not being able to maintain a full-time job was lessened with each story. During this, I realized just how many things people with disabilities have to offer their employers, coworkers, and society as a whole.

People with disabilities, especially those whose conditions began at a young age, have been forced to adapt and persist through even the most strenuous times. We build soft skills such as resilience, courage, and compassion often sooner than our peers. These characteristics were not crafted overnight. These traits were shaped over time through every obstacle or battle our conditions have presented us with throughout the diagnosis and treatment journeys. Companies or managers look for these attributes in their team members. Lucky for us, we've already got them!

A later interview with Phil provided me with another example of the potential positive impacts our conditions can have on our lives, including in our professional endeavors. Phil, who grapples with Type 1 Diabetes, highlighted how his condition served as a motivator for him in his work. "In a lot of ways, I've taken back control of my life regarding my health and how I see the world, and I attack everything with purpose."

He continued, reflecting on his career path: "I've had more promotions, bonuses, and job changes into better roles than I ever had before my diagnosis. Because my diagnosis took so long and I didn't know was wrong with me, I was convinced I was dying. To be honest, I was dying. Getting the diagnosis and finding a way to treat myself was a new lease on life and that's how I've been attacking life ever since."

Steve Bone, a career consultant at Leeds University, helps promote inclusivity to students in their career search after college. In his article about managing the application and hiring process as a person with a disability, he reminds you that you have something extra. In some ways, having a disability can be a barrier, but remember you've also learned valuable soft skills other candidates of the same age likely don't have. He highlights the importance of finding employers who promote diversity and inclusion, specifically focusing on accessibility for team members and clients. Doing your research to find inclusive employers can make the application process easier, when and if you decide to disclose your disabilities.[69]

69   Steve Bone, "Tackling the Application Process & Being Open about a Disability," *My Plus Students' Club* (blog), *My Plus Students' Club*, November 26, 2018.

These stories also highlighted the importance of communication, especially in the workplace. Communication had worked in every other aspect of my life, yet I still decided I was better off not opening up to my supervisors or coworkers about my disabilities. I thought my symptoms would depict me as someone who was weak and always relied on others. After a great deal of research, I'm glad I've been convinced this is hardly the case.

Keep in mind you are responsible for sharing your disability with your employer, if you so choose. In the United States, employers cannot ask if you have a disability as stipulated by the Americans with Disabilities Act. They are only able to ask if you are able to complete the requirements of the job with or without reasonable accommodations.[70] Should you choose to disclose your disability, many factors may arise, such as when to share your condition, what you hope to gain by sharing your disability, and what your rights are in case you face some form of discrimination.

After deciding to disclose your disability or condition to your potential or future employer, it's important to plan when you will share these details at work. I now believe it is better to share later rather than never, but there are pros and cons to each point in the job search process. Your first opportunity to share your disability will likely be at the end of a job application. This question asks for a voluntary self-identification of a disability to ensure equal working rights and a right to reasonable accommodations for people with different abilities.

---

70 "Your Employment Rights as an Individual with a Disability," US Equal Employment Opportunity Commission, accessed February 17, 2021.

As with most other things, it is also your decision of whether you will check the box that states, "yes, I have a disability, or previously had a disability." Some disability blogs encourage disclosing your condition so you can provide the employer advance notice for your accommodations. Others insist to not "admit" to having a disability unless you require specific accommodations for this role, as you may face conscious or unconscious discrimination from your employer because of your disclosure.

While I continue to apply for roles after college, I still switch up my response to this question, as my uncertainty and fear of discrimination comes and goes without reason. In a community in which we rely so heavily on what others with disabilities have done in their lives, it is difficult to not be swayed by the stories others may share. I do wonder what impact this admission may have had on the applications I've sent, but I do my best to not dwell on the what-ifs in these kinds of situations.

I've found waiting to disclose my conditions until I've reached the interview stage has worked best for me. It's at this point I'm able to learn more about the role and its requirements, and I can better understand how my symptoms will impact my work. Because my main symptom is unpredictable full-body pain, my ability to simply sit at a desk for a few hours can be compromised at any time.

When I share this information, I make sure to not dwell on my conditions during the interview. This is a detail I want the employer to be aware of, but it should not be the only thing they focus on when considering my candidacy. I also make sure to come prepared with some ideas on accommodations; should there be any concern about what accommodations the employer or my colleagues may have to make for me, I feel being upfront with my expectations could be helpful to them.

I choose to share my conditions with my employer at an early enough time to determine whether they are respectful and cognizant of my needs. If I feel as though there may be any bias, unconscious or otherwise, I would rather know this ahead of time so I can determine whether I feel comfortable working in this environment. I want my employer and colleagues to be aware of my conditions and corresponding accommodations, but I don't want them to assume I may be incapable of something without seeking my perspective first.

You have an abundance of potential accommodations you can work out with your employer. The hard part is coming together and allowing all parties to express their needs to find compromises for both. By coming into the conversation prepared to discuss your needs *and* your rights, you'll be well-equipped to request accommodations or modifications in the workplace.

The best advice I can give is to research your rights specific to your personal situation, job industry, and condition. The American with Disabilities Act will likely provide the greatest amount of coverage during the job application and hiring process. The ADA emphasizes you must be qualified to perform the essential duties of the job, with or without reasonable accommodation. Under this guideline, you must fulfill the requirements of the role, such as the required education, experience, or skills. So long as you have a disability, a history of a disability, fulfill the requirements of the role, and can complete the essential job functions with or without reasonable accommodation, you are covered against discrimination under the ADA.

It is important to note how the ADA defines reasonable accommodations, as this will shape what you can request from your employer. They've determined reasonable accommodation to be "any change or adjustment to a job or work environment that permits a qualified applicant or employee with a disability to participate in the job application process, to perform the essential functions of a job, or to enjoy benefits and privileges of employment equal to those enjoyed by employees without disabilities."[71] You can request a number of accommodations, like modified work environment or schedule, accessible training materials, and access to modified equipment, just to name a few. Another resource, the Job Accommodation Network (or JAN) has a multitude of accommodation resources and ideas, but it's up to you to determine what will work best for your situation and your role.

Just like every other setting I've gone over, finding a company or specific supervisor who will understand your conditions, how they impact you, and what accommodations you may need at work is crucial. I think once you find one person who will support you, it will be much easier to continue to share your experiences with the rest of your team. By sharing your story with others, you will not only raise awareness about

---

71   Ibid.

disabilities in the office, but you may inspire others to share their experiences as well.

At the end of our interview, Kaitlyn explained to me how she shares her story in the workplace. She is vocal about her condition and the issues she faces and is able to decide how much information she can share with those around her, depending on her relationship with them. She has applied these communication tools to every aspect of her life, including her current job positions at her school, and the majority of the reactions have been accepting and supportive of her and her situation.

As I've continued my role on campus, I've learned keeping my conditions and their symptoms from others is not a sustainable way to work. On my best days, I push past the pain and won't utter a single complaint to others. On my worst days, I'm unable to show up to my shift altogether, or won't function as needed if I can make it in. Over time, I've become more accustomed to managing my role and my disabilities.

I now feel more comfortable opening up to my coworkers, as I'm able to provide more concrete examples of what I may or may not be capable of doing on certain days. I've begun to allow myself to be honest about what I was going through and how my disabilities can impact my work. This revelation has also made an impact on my future job roles as I've begun my post-graduation job search. I'm proud to select the disabilities box on each application now that I know the strength and abilities my disabilities have given me. As time goes on, I look forward to seeing how my newfound willingness to share my conditions will benefit both my well-being and my professional livelihood.

FINAL THOUGHTS

———

When I began my diagnosis and treatment journey, I struggled to find any resources I could rely on to help me through this process. Books given to me by my physicians were far beyond my comprehension as a child. Social media had just started to come into existence as I grew alongside it. My fear of opening up during most of my childhood prevented me from possibly finding another person my age who could relate to my experiences.

I felt isolated growing up without knowing anyone else around me who felt what I was feeling. Because of this loneliness, I had always hoped when I grew older, I would somehow find a way to reach out to other young people with invisible disabilities to prove we are not alone. As an adolescent, I could hardly imagine what I could possibly do to achieve this. I also lacked the self-confidence in myself to understand that I could have an impact on others.

I thought the invisible conversations I held between myself and others in my life were purely for my own benefit. I sought understanding, support, or accommodations for my own needs from my teachers, peers, friends, supervisors, and more. What I didn't know was these conversations would oftentimes be the start to another person's awareness about invisible disabilities, specifically in children and young adults. Those who were accepting and positively curious about my conditions took steps to educate themselves and learn more about my disabilities, or simply invisible disabilities in general.

It feels empowering to know I could motivate people in my life to educate themselves about disabilities of all kinds, hopefully paving the way for more young people who may want to share their experiences with others. And through writing this book and finding others like me, I have learned I am not the only one having these conversations. Some people have the courage to share their story and seek support from others. Determining when and how you may share your disabilities is not easy but adding your voice to the conversation makes our invisible disability community not so invisible after all.

Like our conditions, these conversations are not visible, but their effect will still be felt each time we decide to open up to others. Making an impact on others, or even society in general, does not require some grand plan or act, as raising your voice can have a ripple effect for more people like us. The more conversations we have, the more people we will be able to see—not only for their invisible disability, but for their entire identity.

Throughout the book, I have aimed to show you my pursuit for understanding and compassion from others. We began with speaking with doctors, parents, and family members, who are often the very first to know of our symptoms. These people in our lives see the unfiltered view of what it is like to develop and grapple with a disability. We hope they will also be the first to provide support to us as we begin to consider sharing our conditions with more people in new environments. But before we can speak with others in our personal, academic, and professional lives, we must engage in a sort of internal dialogue to shape how we see ourselves and our disabilities. The way you see yourself and all aspects of your identity, even beyond your conditions, will determine how you share yourself with others.

While many people in our lives can be kind and understanding, you will find others who will not believe or respect your experiences. Building a strong, confident self-image can help you bounce back from these interactions and help you to continue your search for support. This process has also shown me the vital role positively curious people can play in our lives. By transforming awareness into knowledge and understanding, we can find acceptance and support in multiple aspects of our lives. I am grateful for all of the people in my life who have invited me to lean on them as I continued to share my disability with others beyond my support system. They have helped me to move past the many people who doubted and ridiculed my conditions and experiences.

How you share your conditions with others will change over time as you become more comfortable disclosing your disabilities. The lessons I've learned didn't come to me in a linear way, as I faced countless ups and downs in my confidence and commitment to opening up about my disabilities. There are times when it seems easier to simply say nothing at all;

it is easy to give in to the idea that no one cares about what you may be going through.

But I care. The others you've read about in this book care, as well as many more whose stories we've yet to hear. I invite you to try to take comfort in the fact that others understand, or want to understand, what you are going through and want to listen to what you have to say. But it's up to you to find the strength to advocate for yourself and speak up to find those people in your life in all sorts of settings.

Find the tools and methods that work best for you when conversing with parents, doctors, teachers, friends, partners, and so on. Look to those in your support system to encourage you along your journey. Remember you are not expected to explain your condition every time someone asks. Allow yourself to rest from these conversations, as it is an ongoing and taxing process, but make sure to keep trying to have these conversations to get the support you need. You'll soon be able to see the effect on your own life as you gain reliable relationships and accommodations. This individual process contributes to a much greater movement, as your commitment to sharing your conditions impacts the entire invisible disability community.

You have the power to help yourself and many others like you through self-advocacy and communication—so let's start talking.

ACKNOWLEDGMENTS

———

A special acknowledgment to my brother, my uncle, and my partner. Your support means so much to me.

Carla Allen
Isabelle Baurer
Bella Buccilli
Michelle Buslov
Michelle Carroll
Awilda Charriez
Annie Chu
Leigh Claflin
Sam Coleman
Derek Conway
Phillip Cook
Stephanie Curreri
Susanna D'Souza
Robert DeRose
Emma Enright
Kelsey Erstein
Page Flanigan
Camila Flores

Miranda Fry
Kevin Gaffney
Brandon Galeano
Evelyn Galeano
Melanie Galeano
Nelson Galeano
Roman Galeano
Gary Guillot
Judy Guillot
Deedee Haith
Jamison Hill
Stacey Hobbs
Linda Johnson
Melissa Johnson
Stephen Johnson
Jerry Kallas
Vik Kapoor
Ashritha Karuturi
Eric Koester
Arushi Kumar
Madeline Lambert
Glenn Migliozzi
Tiernay Monahan
Johanna Mouyal
Jordan Niedoba
Natalie Oakes
Elianet Oliva
Alison Palmer
Alisa Parenti
Antonio Perez
Brooke Pizzi
Andrew Plifka

Mary Powell
Michaela Salvo
Swarna Shiv
Jennifer Snyder
Janos Stone
Gabrielle Watkins
Emily Weiner
Tiffany Yensel

APPENDIX

——

INTRODUCTION

- Children's Hospital of Philadelphia. "Amplified Musculoskeletal Pain Syndrome (AMPS)." Children's Hospital of Philadelphia. Accessed January 14, 2021. https://www.chop.edu/conditions-diseases/amplified-musculoskeletal-pain-syndrome-amps.

- Disabled World. "Invisible Disabilities: List and General Information." Disabled World. Updated September 10, 2020. https://www.disabled-world.com/disability/types/invisible/.

- Pediatric Rheumatology Special Committee. "Amplified Musculoskeletal Pain Syndrome (AMPS)." American College of Rheumatology. Accessed January 14, 2021. https://www.rheumatology.org/I-Am-A/Patient-Caregiver/Diseases-Conditions/Amplified-Musculoskeletal-Pain-Syndrome-AMPS.

- Providence Medical Center. "AMPS Program Offered at PMC." Providence Medical Center. Accessed January 14, 2021. https://www.providencemedical.com/vnews/display.v/ART/53d98b-09b8cb3.

CHAPTER 1

- Donovan, John. "Talking to Your Doctor: How to Make Yourself Heard." WebMD. Last modified January 27, 2020. https://www.webmd.com/a-to-z-guides/features/be-heard-by-dr#1.

- Weaver, Tristan. "How and Why to Describe Pain Accurately to Your Doctor." The Ohio State University Wexner Medical Center. November 16, 2018. https://wexnermedical.osu.edu/blog/how-and-why-to-describe-pain-accurately-to-your-doctor.

CHAPTER 2

- "5 Minute Guide to Men's Mental Health." Infographic. Mental Health America, accessed January 18, 2021. https://www.mhanational.org/infographic-mental-health-men.

- Anderson, Bebe J., "HIV Stigma and Discrimination Persist, Even in Health Care," *AMA Journal of Ethics* 11, no. 12 (December 2009): 998-1001. https://pubmed.ncbi.nlm.nih.gov/23207098/.

- Armstrong, Katrina, Karima L. Ravenell, Suzanne McMurphy, and Mary Putt. "Racial/Ethnic Differences in Physician Distrust in the United States." *American Journal of Public Health* 97, no. 7 (July 2007): 1283-1289. https://doi.org/10.2105/AJPH.2005.080762.

- Banks, Ian. "No Man's Land: Men, Illness, and the NHS," *The BMJ* 323, no. 7320 (2001): 1058-1060. Banks I. (2001). https://doi.org/10.1136/bmj.323.7320.1058.

- Bridges, Khiara M. "Implicit Bias and Racial Disparities in Health Care." American Bar Association. Accessed January 18, 2021. https://www.americanbar.org/groups/crsj/publications/human_rights_magazine_home/the-state-of-healthcare-in-the-united-states/racial-disparities-in-health-care/.

- Coaston, Jane. "The Intersectionality Wars." *Vox,* May 28, 2019. https://www.vox.com/the-highlight/2019/5/20/18542843/intersectionality-conservatism-law-race-gender-discrimination.

- *Fowler's Dictionary of Modern English Usage,* 4th ed., s.v. "ageism." Oxford: Oxford University Press, 2015. Accessed January 21, 2021, https://www.oxfordreference.com/view/10.1093/acref/9780199661350.001.0001/acref-9780199661350-e-140.

- Gorvett, Zaria. "Why Transgender People Are Ignored by Modern Medicine." *BBC News.* August 16, 2020. https://www.bbc.com/future/article/20200814-why-our-medical-systems-are-ignoring-transgender-people.

- Herek, Gregory M. and John P. Capitanio. "AIDS Stigma and Sexual Prejudice," *The American Behavioral Scientist* 42, no. 7 (April 1999): 1130-1147. http://dx.doi.org.ezproxy.babson.edu/10.1177/0002764299042007006.

- Hoffman, Diane and Anita Tarzian. "The Girl Who Cried Pain: A Bias Against Women in the Treatment of Pain," *The Journal of Law, Medicine & Ethics* 28, no. 4 (2001): 13-14. https://doi.org/10.1111/j.1748-720X.2001.tb00037.x.

- Hoffman, Kelly M., Sophie Trawalter, Jordan R. Axt, and M. Norman Oliver. "Racial Bias in Pain Assessment and Treatment Recommendations, and False Beliefs about Biological Differences between Blacks and Whites." *Proceedings of the National Academies of Sciences* 113, no. 6 (April 2016): 4296-4301. https://doi.org/10.1073/pnas.1516047113.

- Ianzito, Christina. "Why Men Don't Go to the Doctor." AARP. Published September 6, 2019. Accessed January 18, 2021. https://www.aarp.org/health/healthy-living/info-2019/survey-men-avoiding-doctors.html.

- James, E.F. "An Interview with Susan E. Honeyman, Author of: Child Pain, Migraine and Invisible Disability (Routledge 2018)." *Farah Mendlesohn* (blog). *Farah Mendlesohn*, March 14, 2019. https://farahmendlesohn.com/2019/03/14/an-interview-with-susan-a-honeyman-author-of-child-pain-migraine-and-invisible-disability-routledge-2018/.

- Lam, Kristin. "Some Americans Are Denied 'Lifesaving' Health Care Because They Are Transgender." *USA Today*. December 11, 2018. https://www.usatoday.com/story/news/2018/12/11/transgender-health-care-patients-advocates-call-improvements/1829307002/.

- MindWise Innovations. "A Critical Look at Men's Mental Health." *MindWise Innovations Blog & News* (blog). *MindWise Innovations,* accessed January 18, 2021. https://www.mindwise.org/blog/uncategorized/a-critical-look-at-mens-mental-health/.

- NSPCC. "What to Do If a Child Reveals Abuse." Reporting Abuse. Accessed February 25, 2021. https://www.nspcc.org.uk/keeping-children-safe/reporting-abuse/what-to-do-child-reveals-abuse/.

- Ogrodniczuk, John, John Oliffe, David Kuhl, and Paul A. Gross. "Men's Mental Health." *Canadian Family Physician Medecin de Famille Canadien* 62, no. 6 (June 2016): 463-464. https://www.ncbi.nlm.nih.gov/pmc/articles/PMC4907547/.

- Regis College. "Why Ageism in Health Care Is a Growing Concern." *Online Degrees* (blog). *Regis College*, accessed January 19, 2021. https://online.regiscollege.edu/blog/why-ageism-in-health-care-is-a-growing-concern/.

- Rothman, Lily. "The Disturbing History of African-Americans and Medical Research Goes Beyond Henrietta Lacks." *Time*. April 21, 2017. https://time.com/4746297/henrietta-lacks-movie-history-research-oprah/.

- Schopen, Fay. "The Healthcare Gender Bias: Do Men Get Better Medical Treatment?" *The Guardian*, November 20, 2017. https://www.theguardian.com/lifeandstyle/2017/nov/20/healthcare-gender-bias-women-pain.

- Simons, Sandra. "ER Goddess: COVID-19 Lays Bare Racial Bias in Health Care." *Emergency Medicine News* 42, no. 7 (July 2020): 1, 34. https://journals.lww.com/em-news/fulltext/2020/07000/er_goddess__covid_19_lays_bare_racial_bias_in.1.aspx.

- Tello, Monique. "Racism and Discrimination in Health Care: Providers and Patients." *Harvard Health Blog* (blog). *Harvard Health Publishing,* January 16, 2017. https://www.health.harvard.edu/blog/racism-discrimination-health-care-providers-patients-2017011611015.

CHAPTER 3

- Anxiety and Depression Association of America. "Fibromyalgia." Anxiety and Depression Association of America. Accessed January 21, 2021. https://adaa.org/understanding-anxiety/related-illnesses/other-related-conditions/fibromyalgia.

- Griffith, Morgan R. "10 Health Problems Related to Stress That You Can Fix." WebMD. Last modified April 1, 2014. https://www.webmd.com/balance/stress-management/features/10-fixable-stress-related-health-problems#1.

- Invisible Disabilities Association. "What Is an Invisible Disability?" Invisible Disabilities Association. Accessed January 21, 2021. https://invisibledisabilities.org/what-is-an-invisible-disability/.

- Lattie, Emily G., Sarah Ketchen Lipson, and Daniel Eisenberg. "Technology and College Student Mental Health: Challenges and Opportunities." *Frontiers in Psychiatry* 10, no. 246 (April 2019): 1-5. https://doi.org/10.3389/fpsyt.2019.00246.

- Mayo Clinic. "Fibromyalgia." Mayo Clinic. Accessed January 21, 2021. https://www.mayoclinic.org/diseases-conditions/fibromyalgia/symptoms-causes/syc-20354780.

- Mental Health America. "31 Tips to Boost Your Mental Health." Mental Health America. Accessed January 21, 2021. https://www.mhanational.org/31-tips-boost-your-mental-health.

- Mental Health Foundation. "How to Look after Your Mental Health." Mental Health Foundation. Accessed January 21, 2021. https://www.mentalhealth.org.uk/publications/how-to-mental-health.

- National Institute of Mental Health. "Mental Illness." Statistics. Last modified January, 2021. https://www.nimh.nih.gov/health/statistics/mental-illness.shtml#part_154910.

CHAPTER 4

- Hoghughi, Masud. "The Importance of Parenting in Child Health." *The BMJ* 316, no. 7144 (May 1998): 1545-1550. https://doi.org/10.1136/bmj.316.7144.1545.

- Roland, James. "Everything You Should Know About Allodynia." Healthline. Last modified August 21, 2018. https://www.healthline.com/health/allodynia.

- Thomas, Jodi. "Dr. Leora Kuttner: A Pediatric Pain Pioneer and Champion for Kids All Over the World." *The Meg Foundation* (blog). *The Meg Foundation*, October 21, 2020. https://www.megfoundationforpain.org/blog/dr-leora-kuttner-has-pioneered-and-transformed-the-world-of-pediatric-pain.

CHAPTER 6

- Ben-Zeév, Aaron. "Do Not Pity Me." Psychology Today. August 14, 2010. https://www.psychologytoday.com/us/blog/in-the-name-love/201008/do-not-pity-me.

- Indeed. "Active Listening Skills: Definition and Examples." Indeed Career Guide. November 23, 2020. https://www.indeed.com/career-advice/career-development/active-listening-skills.

- Katrivesis, Maria and Barbel Winter. "Active Listening—Unconditional Positive Regard Across Cultures." Sydney: futures Upfront, 2016. https://www.nds.org.au/images/resources/person-centred/Active-listening.pdf, futures Upfront.

- Quote Seed. "'Pity Costs Nothing and Ain't Worth Nothing.' —Josh Billings." Quotes. Accessed January 28, 2021. http://quoteseed.com/quotes/josh-billings/josh-billings-pity-costs-nothing-and-aint-worth/.

- University of California, Los Angeles. "Burden vs. Entitlement: A Disabled Person's Internal Battle." Office of Information Technology Disabilities and Computing Program. Accessed January 28, 2021. https://dcp.ucla.edu/node/88.

CHAPTER 7

- ADA.gov. "Information and Technical Assistance on the Americans with Disabilities Act." United States Department of Justice Civil Rights Division. Accessed February 5, 2021. https://www.ada.gov/ada_intro.htm.

- Center for Parent Information & Resources. "Supports, Modifications, and Accommodations for Students." February 8, 2020. https://www.parentcenterhub.org/accommodations/.

- Morin, Amanda. "Common Accommodations and Modifications in School." Understood for All Inc. Accessed February 5, 2021. https://www.understood.org/en/learning-thinking-differences/treatments-approaches/educational-strategies/common-classroom-accommodations-and-modifications.

- National Center for Learning Disabilities. "Accommodations for Students with LD." LD Online. Accessed February 5, 2021. http://www.ldonline.org/article/8022/.

- Southwest ADA Center. "Disability Rights Laws in Public Primary and Secondary Education: How Do They Relate?" ADA National Network. Accessed February 5, 2021. https://adata.org/factsheet/disability-rights-laws-public-primary-and-secondary-education-how-do-they-relate.

- US Department of Education. "About IDEA." Individuals with Disabilities Education Act. Accessed February 5, 2021. https://sites.ed.gov/idea/about-idea/.

- US Department of Health and Human Services. "Your Rights Under Section 504 of the Rehabilitation Act." Office for Civil Rights. Revised June, 2006. https://www.hhs.gov/sites/default/files/ocr/civilrights/resources/factsheets/504.pdf.

CHAPTER 8

- Finch, Sam Dylan. "5 Lessons I've Learned as the Partner of Someone with an Invisible Disability." *Everyday Feminism.* July 2, 2015. https://everydayfeminism.com/2015/07/partner-invisible-disability/.

CHAPTER 9

- Bone, Steve. "Tackling the Application Process & Being Open about a Disability." *My Plus Students' Club* (blog). *My Plus Students' Club*, November 26, 2018. https://myplusstudentsclub.com/blog/tackling-the-application-process-being-open-about-a-disability/.

- US Equal Employment Opportunity Commission. "Your Employment Rights as an Individual with a Disability." US Equal Employment Opportunity Commission. Accessed February 17, 2021. https://www.eeoc.gov/laws/guidance/your-employment-rights-individual-disability.